ALEKS Math Exercise Book

2023

A Comprehensive Workbook

+ ALEKS Math Practice Tests

By

Reza Nazari

All inquiries should be addressed to:

info@EffortlessMath.com

www.EffortlessMath.com

ISBN-13: 978-1-63719-199-6

Published by: **Effortless Math Education Inc.**

For Online Math Practice Visit www.EffortlessMath.com

Welcome to
ALEKS Math Prep
2023

Thank you for choosing Effortless Math for your ALEKS Math test preparation and congratulations on making the decision to take the ALEKS test! It's a remarkable move you are taking, one that shouldn't be diminished in any capacity.

That's why you need to use every tool possible to ensure you succeed on the test with the highest possible score, and this extensive math workbook is one such tool.

If math has never been a strong subject for you, don't worry! This book along with our online ALEKS Math resources will help you prepare for (and even ACE) the ALEKS Math test. As test day draws nearer, effective preparation becomes increasingly more important. Thankfully, you have this comprehensive workbook to help you get ready for the test. With this book and Effortless Math online resources, you can feel confident that you will be more than ready for the ALEKS Math test when the time comes.

First and foremost, it is important to note that this book is a workbook and not a textbook. Every lesson of this practice book was carefully developed to ensure that you are making the most effective use of your time while preparing for the test. This up-to-date book reflects the 2023 test guidelines and will put you on the right track to hone your math skills, overcome exam anxiety, and boost your confidence, so that you do your best to succeed on the ALEKS Math test.

This exercise book will:

☑ Explain the format of the ALEKS Math test.

☑ Describe specific test-taking strategies that you can use on the test.

☑ Provide ALEKS Math test-taking tips.

☑ Help you identify the areas in which you need to concentrate your study time.

☑ Offer exercises that help you develop the basic math skills you will learn in each section.

☑ Give **2 realistic and full-length practice tests** (featuring new question types) with detailed answers to help you measure your exam readiness and build confidence.

This resource contains comprehensive practice questions and exercises that you will need to prepare for the ALEKS Math test. You'll get numerous skill building exercises as well as tips and techniques on how to prepare for your ALEKS math test.

In addition, in the following pages you'll find:

➤ **How to Use This Book Effectively** – This section provides you with step-by-step instructions on how to get the most out of this comprehensive study guide.

➤ **How to study for the ALEKS Math Test** – A six-step study program has been developed to help you make the best use of this book and prepare for your ALEKS Math test. Here you'll find tips and strategies to guide your study program and help you understand ALEKS Math and how to ace the test.

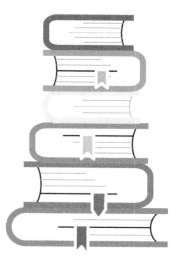

➤ **ALEKS Math Review** – Learn everything you need to know about the ALEKS Math test.

➤ **ALEKS Math Test-Taking Strategies** – Learn how to effectively put these recommended test-taking techniques into use for improving your ALEKS Math score.

➤ **Test Day Tips** – Review these tips to make sure you will do your best when the big day comes.

Effortless Math's ALEKS Online Center

Effortless Math Online ALEKS Center offers a complete study program, including the following:

✓ Step-by-step instructions on how to prepare for the ALEKS Math test

✓ Numerous ALEKS Math worksheets to help you measure your math skills

✓ Complete list of ALEKS Math formulas

✓ Video lessons for all ALEKS Math topics

✓ Full-length ALEKS Math practice tests

✓ And much more…

No Registration Required.

Visit **EffortlessMath.com/ALEKS** to find your online ALEKS Math resources.

How to Use This Book Effectively

Look no further when you need a study program to improve your math skills to succeed on the math portion of the ALEKS test. Each chapter of this comprehensive workbook will provide you with the knowledge, tools, and understanding needed for every topic covered on the test.

It's imperative that you understand each topic before moving onto another one, as that's the way to guarantee your success. You can use Effortless Math online course (a free course) to find examples and a step-by-step guide of every math concept in this workbook to better understand the content that will be on the test. To get the best possible results from this book:

> **Begin studying long before your test date.** This provides you ample time to learn the different math concepts. The earlier you begin studying for the test, the sharper your skills will be. Do not procrastinate! Provide yourself with plenty of time to learn the concepts and feel comfortable that you understand them when your test date arrives.

> **Practice consistently.** Study ALEKS Math concepts at least 20 to 30 minutes a day. Remember, slow and steady wins the race, which can be applied to preparing for the ALEKS Math test. Instead of cramming to tackle everything at once, be patient and learn the math topics in short bursts.

> Whenever you get a math problem wrong, **mark it off, and review it later** to make sure you understand the concept.

> Start each session by **looking over the previous material.**

> Once you've reviewed the book's exercises, **take a practice test at the back of the book** to gauge your level of readiness. Then, review your results. Read detailed answers and solutions for each question you missed.

> **Take another practice test** to get an idea of how ready you are to take the actual exam. Taking the practice tests will give you the confidence you need on test day. Simulate the ALEKS testing environment by sitting in a quiet room free from distraction. Make sure to clock yourself with a timer.

How to Study for the ALEKS Math Test

Studying for the ALEKS Math test can be a really daunting and boring task. What's the best way to go about it? Is there a certain study method that works better than others? Well, studying for the ALEKS Math can be done effectively. The following six-step program has been designed to make preparing for the ALEKS Math test more efficient and less overwhelming.

Step **1** - Create a study plan
Step **2** - Choose your study resources
Step **3** - Review, Learn, Practice
Step **4** - Learn and practice test-taking strategies
Step **5** - Learn the ALEKS Test format and take practice tests
Step **6** - Analyze your performance

STEP 1: Create a Study Plan

It's always easier to get things done when you have a plan. Creating a study plan for the ALEKS Math test can help you to stay on track with your studies. It's important to sit down and prepare a study plan with what works with your life, work, and any other obligations you may have. Devote enough time each day to studying. It's also a great idea to break down each section of the exam into blocks and study one concept at a time.

It's important to understand that there is no "right" way to create a study plan. Your study plan will be personalized based on your specific needs and learning style.

Follow these guidelines to create an effective study plan for your ALEKS Math test:

★ **Analyze your learning style and study habits** – Everyone has a different learning style. It is essential to embrace your individuality and the unique way you learn. Think about what works and what doesn't work for you. Do you prefer ALEKS Math prep books or a combination of textbooks and video lessons? Does it work better for you if you study every night for thirty minutes or is it more effective to study in the morning before going to work?

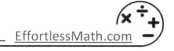

★ **Evaluate your schedule** – Review your current schedule and find out how much time you can consistently devote to ALEKS Math study.

★ **Develop a schedule** – Now it's time to add your study schedule to your calendar like any other obligation. Schedule time for study, practice, and review. Plan out which topic you will study on which day to ensure that you're devoting enough time to each concept. Develop a study plan that is mindful, realistic, and flexible.

★ **Stick to your schedule** – A study plan is only effective when it is followed consistently. You should try to develop a study plan that you can follow for the length of your study program.

★ **Evaluate your study plan and adjust as needed** – Sometimes you need to adjust your plan when you have new commitments. Check in with yourself regularly to make sure that you're not falling behind in your study plan. Remember, the most important thing is sticking to your plan. Your study plan is all about helping you be more productive. If you find that your study plan is not as effective as you want, don't get discouraged. It's okay to make changes as you figure out what works best for you.

STEP 2: Choose Your Study Resources

There are numerous textbooks and online resources available for the ALEKS Math test, and it may not be clear where to begin. Don't worry! This exercise book reviews all ALEKS Math concepts and topics. In addition to the book content, you can also use Effortless Math's online resources. (video lessons, worksheets, formulas, etc.) On each page, there is a link 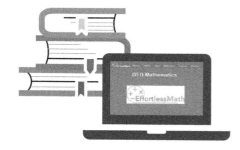 (and a QR code) to an online webpage which provides a comprehensive review of the topic, step-by-step instruction, video tutorial, and numerous examples and exercises to help you fully understand the concept.

Simply visit <u>EffortlessMath.com/ALEKS</u> to find your online ALEKS Math resources.

STEP 3: Review, Learn, Practice

This ALEKS Math exercise book breaks down each subject into specific skills or content areas. For instance, the percent concept is separated into different topics—percent calculation, percent increase and decrease, percent problems, etc. Use this book to help you go over all key math concepts and topics on the ALEKS Math test.

As you review each topic, take notes or highlight the concepts you would like to go over again in the future. If you're unfamiliar with a topic or something is difficult for you, use the link (or the QR code) at the top of the page to find the webpage that provides more instruction about that topic. For each math topic, plenty of instructions, step-by-step guides, and examples are provided to ensure you get a good grasp of the material.

Quickly review the topics you do understand to get a brush-up of the material. Be sure to do the practice questions provided at the end of every chapter to measure your understanding of the concepts.

STEP 4: Learn and Practice Test-taking Strategies

In the following sections, you will find important test-taking strategies and tips that can help you earn extra points. You'll learn how to think strategically and when to guess if you don't know the answer to a question. Using ALEKS Math test-taking strategies and tips can help you raise your score and do well on the test. Apply test taking strategies on the practice tests to help you boost your confidence.

STEP 5: Learn the ALEKS Test Format and Take Practice Tests

The *ALEKS Test Review* section provides information about the structure of the ALEKS test. Read this section to learn more about the ALEKS test structure, different test sections, the number of questions in each section, and the section time limits. When you have a prior understanding of the test format and different types of ALEKS Math questions, you'll feel more confident when you take the actual exam.

Once you have read through the instructions and lessons and feel like you are ready to go – take advantage of both of the full-length ALEKS Math practice tests available in this exercise book. Use the practice tests to sharpen your skills and build confidence.

The ALEKS Math practice tests offered at the end of the book are formatted similarly to the actual ALEKS Math test. When you take each practice test, try to simulate actual testing conditions. To take the practice tests, sit in a quiet space, time yourself, and work through as many of the questions as time allows. The practice tests are followed by detailed answer explanations to help you find your weak areas, learn from your mistakes, and raise your ALEKS Math score.

STEP 6: Analyze Your Performance

After taking the practice tests, look over the answer keys and explanations to learn which questions you answered correctly and which you did not. Never be discouraged if you make a few mistakes. See them as a learning opportunity. This will highlight your strengths and weaknesses.

You can use the results to determine if you need additional practice or if you are ready to take the actual ALEKS Math test.

Looking for more?

Visit <u>EffortlessMath.com/ALEKS</u> to find hundreds of ALEKS Math worksheets, video tutorials, practice tests, ALEKS Math formulas, and much more.

Or scan this QR code.

No Registration Required.

ALEKS Test Review

ALEKS (Assessment and Learning in Knowledge Spaces) is an artificial intelligence-based assessment tool to measure the strengths and weaknesses of a student's mathematical knowledge. ALEKS is available for a variety of subjects and courses in K-12, Higher Education, and Continuing Education. The findings of ALEKS's assessment test help to find an appropriate level for course placement. The ALEKS math placement assessment ensures students' readiness for particular math courses at colleges.

ALEKS does not use multiple-choice questions like most other standardized tests. Instead, it utilizes adaptable and easy-to-use method that mimic paper and pencil techniques. When taking the ALEKS test, a brief tutorial helps you learn how to use ALEKS answer input tools. You then begin the ALEKS Assessment. In about 30 to 45 minutes, the test measures your current content knowledge by asking 20 to 30 questions. ALEKS is a Computer Adaptive (CA) assessment. It means that each question will be chosen on the basis of answers to all the previous questions. Therefore, each set of assessment questions is unique. The ALEKS Math assessment does not allow you to use a personal calculator. But for some questions ALEKS onscreen calculator button is active and the test taker can use it.

Key Features of the ALEKS Mathematics Assessment

Some key features of the ALEKS Math assessment are:

❖ Mathematics questions on ALEKS are adaptive to identify the student's knowledge from a comprehensive standard curriculum, ranging from basic arithmetic up to precalculus, including trigonometry but not calculus.

❖ Unlike other standardized tests, the ALEKS assessment does not provide a "grade" or "raw score." Instead, ALEKS identifies which concepts the student has mastered and what topics the student needs to learn.

❖ ALEKS does not use multiple-choice questions. Instead, students need to produce authentic mathematical input.

❖ There is no time limit for taking the ALEKS Math assessment. But it usually takes 30 to 45 minutes to complete the assessment.

The ALEKS Math score is between 1 and 100 and is interpreted as a percentage correct. A higher ALEKS score indicates that the test-taker has mastered more math concepts. ALEKS Math assessment tool evaluates mastery of a comprehensive set of mathematics skills ranging from basic arithmetic up to precalculus, including trigonometry but not calculus. It will place students in classes up to Calculus.

ALEKS Math Test-Taking Strategies

Here are some test-taking strategies that you can use to maximize your performance and results on the ALEKS Math test.

#1: USE THIS APPROACH TO ANSWER EVERY ALEKS MATH QUESTION

- Review the question to identify keywords and important information.

- Translate the keywords into math operations so you can solve the problem.

- Review the answer choices. What are the differences between answer choices?

- Draw or label a diagram if needed.

- Try to find patterns.

- Find the right method to answer the question. Use straightforward math, plug in numbers, or test the answer choices (backsolving).

- Double-check your work.

#2: ANSWER EVERY ALEKS MATH QUESTION

Don't leave any fields empty! ALEKS is a Computer Adaptive (CA) assessment. Therefore, you cannot leave a question unanswered and you cannot go back to previous questions.

Even if you're unable to work out a problem, strive to answer it. Take a guess if you have to. You will not lose points by getting an answer wrong, though you may gain a point by getting it correct!

#3: BALLPARK

A ballpark answer is a rough approximation. When we become overwhelmed by calculations and figures, we end up making silly mistakes. A decimal that is moved by one unit can change an answer from right to wrong, regardless of the number of steps that you went through to get it. That's where ballparking can play a big part.

If you think you know what the correct answer may be (even if it's just a ballpark answer), you'll usually have the ability to estimate the range of possible answers and avoid simple mistakes.

#4: PLUGGING IN NUMBERS

"Plugging in numbers" is a strategy that can be applied to a wide range of different math problems on the ALEKS Math test. This approach is typically used to simplify a challenging question so that it is more understandable. By using the strategy carefully, you can find the answer without too much trouble.

The concept is fairly straightforward–replace unknown variables in a problem with certain values. When selecting a number, consider the following:

- Choose a number that's basic (just not too basic). Generally, you should avoid choosing 1 (or even 0). A decent choice is 2.

- Try not to choose a number that is displayed in the problem.

- Make sure you keep your numbers different if you need to choose at least two of them.

- If your question contains fractions, then a potential right answer may involve either an LCD (least common denominator) or an LCD multiple.

- 100 is the number you should choose when you are dealing with problems involving percentages.

ALEKS Mathematics – Test Day Tips

After practicing and reviewing all the math concepts you've been taught, and taking some ALEKS mathematics practice tests, you'll be prepared for test day. Consider the following tips to be extra-ready come test time.

Before Your Test

What to do the night before:

- **Relax!** One day before your test, study lightly or skip studying altogether. You shouldn't attempt to learn something new, either. There are plenty of reasons why studying the evening before a big test can work against you. Put it this way— a marathoner wouldn't go out for a sprint before the day of a big race. Mental marathoners—such as yourself—should not study for any more than one hour 24 hours before a ALEKS test. That's because your brain requires some rest to be at its best. The night before your exam, spend some time with family or friends, or read a book.

- **Avoid bright screens** - You'll have to get some good shuteye the night before your test. Bright screens (such as the ones coming from your laptop, TV, or mobile device) should be avoided altogether. Staring at such a screen will keep your brain up, making it hard to drift asleep at a reasonable hour.

- **Make sure your dinner is healthy** - The meal that you have for dinner should be nutritious. Be sure to drink plenty of water as well. Load up on your complex carbohydrates, much like a marathon runner would do. Pasta, rice, and potatoes are ideal options here, as are vegetables and protein sources.

- **Get your bag ready for test day** – Prefer to take ALEKS in the Testing Office? The night prior to your test, pack your bag with your stationery, admissions pass, ID, and any other gear that you need. Keep the bag right by your front door. If you prefer to take the test at home, find a quite place without any distractions.

- **Make plans to reach the testing site** – If you are taking the test at the testing office, ensure that you understand precisely how you will arrive at the site of the test. If parking is something you'll have to find first, plan for it. If you're dependent on public transit, then review the schedule. You should also make sure that the train/bus/subway/streetcar you use will be running. Find out about road closures as well. If a parent or friend is accompanying you, ensure that they understand what steps they have to take as well.

The Day of the Test

- Get up reasonably early, but not too early.

- **Have breakfast** - Breakfast improves your concentration, memory, and mood. As such, make sure the breakfast that you eat in the morning is healthy. The last thing you want to be is distracted by a grumbling tummy. If it's not your own stomach making those noises, another test taker close to you might be instead. Prevent discomfort or embarrassment by consuming a healthy breakfast. Bring a snack with you if you think you'll need it.

- **Follow your daily routine** - Do you watch TV in the morning while getting ready for the day? Don't break your usual habits on the day of the test. Likewise, if coffee isn't something you drink in the morning, then don't take up the habit hours before your test. Routine consistency lets you concentrate on the main objective—doing the best you can on your test.

- **Wear layers** - Dress yourself up in comfortable layers if you are taking the test at the testing site. You should be ready for any kind of internal temperature. If it gets too warm during the test, take a layer off.

- **Make your voice heard** - If something is off, speak to a proctor. If medical attention is needed or if you'll require anything, consult the proctor prior to the start of the test. Any doubts you have should be clarified. You should be entering the test site with a state of mind that is completely clear.

- **Have faith in yourself** - When you feel confident, you will be able to perform at your best. When you are waiting for the test to begin, envision yourself receiving an outstanding result. Try to see yourself as someone who knows all the answers, no matter what the questions are. A lot of athletes tend to use this technique— particularly before a big competition. Your expectations will be reflected by your performance.

During your test

- **Be calm and breathe deeply** - You need to relax before the test, and some deep breathing will go a long way to help you do that. Be confident and calm. You got this. Everybody feels a little stressed out just before an evaluation of any kind is set to begin. Learn some effective breathing exercises. Spend a minute meditating

before the test starts. Filter out any negative thoughts you have. Exhibit confidence when having such thoughts.

- **Concentrate on the test** - Refrain from comparing yourself to anyone else. You shouldn't be distracted by the people near you or random noise. Concentrate exclusively on the test. If you find yourself irritated by surrounding noises, earplugs can be used to block sounds off close to you. Don't forget—the test is going to last an hour or more. Some of that time will be dedicated to brief sections. Concentrate on the specific section you are working on during a particular moment. Do not let your mind wander off to upcoming or previous questions.

- **Try to answer each question individually** - Focus only on the question you are working on. Use one of the test-taking strategies to solve the problem. If you aren't able to come up with an answer, don't get frustrated. Simply guess, then move onto the next question.

- **Don't forget to breathe!** Whenever you notice your mind wandering, your stress levels boosting, or frustration brewing, take a thirty-second break. Shut your eyes, drop your pencil, breathe deeply, and let your shoulders relax. You will end up being more productive when you allow yourself to relax for a moment.

After your test

- **Take it easy** - You will need to set some time aside to relax and decompress once the test has concluded. There is no need to stress yourself out about what you could've said, or what you may have done wrong. At this point, there's nothing you can do about it. Your energy and time would be better spent on something that will bring you happiness for the remainder of your day.

- **Redoing the test** - Did you succeed on the test? Congratulations! Your hard work paid off! Succeeding on this test means that you are now ready to take college level courses.

If you didn't receive the result you expected, though, don't worry! The test can be retaken. In such cases, you will need to follow the retake policy. You also need to re-register to take the exam again.

Contents

Chapter 1: Fractions and Mixed Numbers

Math Topics that you'll learn in this Chapter:

- ✓ Simplifying Fractions
- ✓ Adding and Subtracting Fractions
- ✓ Multiplying and Dividing Fractions
- ✓ Adding Mixed Numbers
- ✓ Subtracting Mixed Numbers
- ✓ Multiplying Mixed Numbers
- ✓ Dividing Mixed Numbers

24

Simplifying Fractions

✎ *Simplify each fraction to its lowest terms.*

1) $\frac{9}{18} =$

2) $\frac{8}{10} =$

3) $\frac{6}{8} =$

4) $\frac{5}{20} =$

5) $\frac{18}{24} =$

6) $\frac{6}{9} =$

7) $\frac{12}{15} =$

8) $\frac{4}{16} =$

9) $\frac{18}{36} =$

10) $\frac{6}{42} =$

11) $\frac{13}{39} =$

12) $\frac{21}{28} =$

13) $\frac{63}{77} =$

14) $\frac{36}{40} =$

15) $\frac{21}{63} =$

16) $\frac{30}{84} =$

17) $\frac{50}{125} =$

18) $\frac{72}{108} =$

19) $\frac{49}{112} =$

20) $\frac{240}{320} =$

21) $\frac{120}{150} =$

✎ *Solve each problem.*

22) Which of the following fractions equal to $\frac{4}{5}$? _____

   A. $\frac{64}{75}$ B. $\frac{92}{115}$ C. $\frac{60}{85}$ D. $\frac{160}{220}$

23) Which of the following fractions equal to $\frac{3}{7}$? _____

   A. $\frac{63}{147}$ B. $\frac{75}{182}$ C. $\frac{54}{140}$ D. $\frac{39}{98}$

24) Which of the following fractions equal to $\frac{2}{9}$? _____

   A. $\frac{84}{386}$ B. $\frac{52}{234}$ C. $\frac{96}{450}$ D. $\frac{112}{522}$

Adding and Subtracting Fractions

✏️ **Find the sum.**

1) $\frac{1}{3} + \frac{2}{3} =$

2) $\frac{1}{2} + \frac{1}{3} =$

3) $\frac{2}{5} + \frac{1}{2} =$

4) $\frac{3}{7} + \frac{2}{3} =$

5) $\frac{3}{4} + \frac{2}{5} =$

6) $\frac{3}{5} + \frac{1}{5} =$

7) $\frac{5}{9} + \frac{1}{2} =$

8) $\frac{3}{5} + \frac{3}{8} =$

9) $\frac{5}{9} + \frac{3}{7} =$

10) $\frac{5}{11} + \frac{1}{4} =$

11) $\frac{3}{7} + \frac{1}{6} =$

12) $\frac{3}{14} + \frac{3}{4} =$

✏️ **Find the difference.**

13) $\frac{1}{2} - \frac{1}{3} =$

14) $\frac{4}{5} - \frac{2}{3} =$

15) $\frac{2}{3} - \frac{1}{6} =$

16) $\frac{3}{5} - \frac{1}{2} =$

17) $\frac{8}{9} - \frac{2}{5} =$

18) $\frac{4}{7} - \frac{1}{9} =$

19) $\frac{2}{5} - \frac{1}{4} =$

20) $\frac{5}{8} - \frac{2}{6} =$

21) $\frac{4}{15} - \frac{1}{10} =$

22) $\frac{7}{20} - \frac{1}{5} =$

23) $\frac{3}{18} - \frac{1}{12} =$

24) $\frac{9}{24} - \frac{3}{16} =$

25) $\frac{3}{7} - \frac{2}{5} =$

26) $\frac{5}{9} - \frac{1}{6} =$

27) $\frac{2}{5} - \frac{1}{10} =$

28) $\frac{5}{12} - \frac{2}{9} =$

29) $\frac{2}{13} - \frac{3}{7} =$

30) $\frac{4}{11} - \frac{5}{8} =$

Multiplying and Dividing Fractions

✏ **Find the value of each expression in lowest terms.**

1) $\frac{1}{2} \times \frac{3}{4} =$

2) $\frac{3}{5} \times \frac{2}{3} =$

3) $\frac{1}{4} \times \frac{2}{5} =$

4) $\frac{1}{6} \times \frac{4}{5} =$

5) $\frac{1}{5} \times \frac{1}{4} =$

6) $\frac{2}{5} \times \frac{1}{2} =$

7) $\frac{7}{9} \times \frac{1}{3} =$

8) $\frac{5}{7} \times \frac{3}{8} =$

9) $\frac{8}{9} \times \frac{6}{7} =$

10) $\frac{5}{6} \times \frac{3}{5} =$

11) $\frac{3}{8} \times \frac{1}{9} =$

12) $\frac{1}{12} \times \frac{3}{7} =$

✏ **Find the value of each expression in lowest terms.**

13) $\frac{1}{2} \div \frac{1}{4} =$

14) $\frac{1}{3} \div \frac{1}{2} =$

15) $\frac{2}{5} \div \frac{1}{3} =$

16) $\frac{1}{4} \div \frac{2}{3} =$

17) $\frac{1}{5} \div \frac{3}{10} =$

18) $\frac{2}{7} \div \frac{1}{3} =$

19) $\frac{3}{5} \div \frac{5}{9} =$

20) $\frac{2}{23} \div \frac{2}{9} =$

21) $\frac{4}{13} \div \frac{1}{4} =$

22) $\frac{9}{14} \div \frac{3}{7} =$

23) $\frac{8}{15} \div \frac{2}{5} =$

24) $\frac{2}{9} \div \frac{7}{11} =$

25) $\frac{2}{5} \div \frac{3}{4} =$

26) $\frac{4}{11} \div \frac{2}{5} =$

27) $\frac{2}{15} \div \frac{5}{8} =$

28) $\frac{3}{10} \div \frac{2}{5} =$

29) $\frac{4}{5} \div \frac{3}{7} =$

30) $\frac{2}{11} \div \frac{3}{5} =$

Adding Mixed Numbers

✏️ **Solve and write the answer in lowest terms**

1) $1\frac{1}{5} + 2\frac{2}{5} =$

2) $1\frac{1}{2} + 4\frac{5}{6} =$

3) $2\frac{4}{5} + 2\frac{3}{10} =$

4) $3\frac{1}{6} + 2\frac{2}{5} =$

5) $1\frac{5}{6} + 1\frac{2}{5} =$

6) $3\frac{5}{7} + 1\frac{2}{9} =$

7) $3\frac{5}{8} + 2\frac{1}{3} =$

8) $1\frac{6}{7} + 3\frac{2}{9} =$

9) $2\frac{5}{9} + 1\frac{1}{4} =$

10) $3\frac{7}{9} + 2\frac{5}{6} =$

11) $2\frac{1}{10} + 2\frac{2}{5} =$

12) $1\frac{3}{10} + 3\frac{4}{5} =$

13) $3\frac{1}{12} + 2\frac{1}{3} =$

14) $5\frac{1}{11} + 1\frac{1}{2} =$

15) $3\frac{1}{21} + 2\frac{2}{3} =$

16) $4\frac{1}{24} + 1\frac{5}{8} =$

17) $2\frac{1}{25} + 3\frac{3}{5} =$

18) $3\frac{1}{15} + 2\frac{2}{10} =$

19) $5\frac{6}{7} + 2\frac{1}{3} =$

20) $2\frac{1}{8} + 3\frac{3}{4} =$

21) $2\frac{5}{7} + 2\frac{2}{21} =$

22) $4\frac{1}{6} + 1\frac{4}{5} =$

23) $2\frac{1}{7} + 2\frac{3}{8} =$

24) $3\frac{1}{4} + 2\frac{2}{3} =$

25) $1\frac{1}{13} + 2\frac{3}{4} =$

26) $3\frac{2}{35} + 2\frac{5}{7} =$

Subtracting Mixed Numbers

✎ **Solve and write the answer in lowest terms.**

1) $5\frac{2}{9} - 2\frac{1}{9} =$

2) $6\frac{2}{7} - 2\frac{1}{3} =$

3) $5\frac{3}{8} - 2\frac{3}{4} =$

4) $7\frac{2}{5} - 3\frac{1}{10} =$

5) $9\frac{5}{7} - 7\frac{4}{21} =$

6) $11\frac{7}{12} - 9\frac{5}{6} =$

7) $9\frac{5}{9} - 8\frac{1}{8} =$

8) $13\frac{7}{9} - 11\frac{3}{7} =$

9) $8\frac{7}{12} - 7\frac{3}{8} =$

10) $11\frac{5}{9} - 9\frac{1}{4} =$

11) $6\frac{5}{6} - 2\frac{2}{9} =$

12) $5\frac{7}{8} - 4\frac{1}{3} =$

13) $9\frac{5}{8} - 8\frac{1}{2} =$

14) $4\frac{9}{16} - 2\frac{1}{4} =$

15) $3\frac{2}{3} - 1\frac{2}{15} =$

16) $5\frac{1}{2} - 4\frac{2}{17} =$

17) $5\frac{6}{7} - 2\frac{1}{3} =$

18) $3\frac{3}{7} - 2\frac{2}{21} =$

19) $7\frac{3}{10} - 5\frac{2}{15} =$

20) $4\frac{5}{6} - 2\frac{2}{9} =$

21) $6\frac{3}{7} - 2\frac{2}{9} =$

22) $7\frac{4}{5} - 6\frac{3}{7} =$

23) $12\frac{3}{7} - 8\frac{1}{3} =$

24) $5\frac{4}{9} - 2\frac{5}{6} =$

25) $10\frac{1}{28} - 7\frac{3}{4} =$

26) $11\frac{5}{12} - 7\frac{5}{48} =$

Multiplying Mixed Numbers

✎ **Solve and write the answer in lowest terms**

1) $1\frac{1}{6} \times 1\frac{3}{7} =$

2) $5\frac{1}{6} \times 2\frac{1}{4} =$

3) $3\frac{3}{7} \times 1\frac{2}{9} =$

4) $3\frac{3}{8} \times 3\frac{1}{6} =$

5) $1\frac{1}{2} \times 5\frac{2}{3} =$

6) $3\frac{1}{2} \times 6\frac{2}{3} =$

7) $9\frac{1}{2} \times 2\frac{1}{6} =$

8) $2\frac{5}{8} \times 8\frac{3}{5} =$

9) $3\frac{4}{5} \times 4\frac{2}{3} =$

10) $5\frac{1}{3} \times 2\frac{2}{7} =$

11) $6\frac{1}{3} \times 3\frac{3}{4} =$

12) $7\frac{2}{3} \times 1\frac{8}{9} =$

13) $8\frac{1}{2} \times 2\frac{1}{6} =$

14) $4\frac{1}{5} \times 8\frac{2}{3} =$

15) $3\frac{1}{8} \times 5\frac{2}{3} =$

16) $2\frac{2}{7} \times 6\frac{2}{5} =$

17) $2\frac{3}{8} \times 7\frac{2}{3} =$

18) $1\frac{7}{8} \times 8\frac{2}{3} =$

19) $9\frac{1}{2} \times 3\frac{1}{5} =$

20) $2\frac{5}{8} \times 4\frac{1}{3} =$

21) $6\frac{1}{3} \times 3\frac{2}{5} =$

22) $5\frac{3}{4} \times 2\frac{2}{7} =$

23) $8\frac{1}{6} \times 2\frac{2}{7} =$

24) $4\frac{1}{6} \times 7\frac{1}{5} =$

25) $2\frac{1}{5} \times 2\frac{5}{8} =$

26) $6\frac{2}{3} \times 4\frac{3}{5} =$

bit.ly/3aPy7XJ

Find more at

Dividing Mixed Numbers

✍ *Solve and write the answer in lowest terms*

1) $6\frac{1}{2} \div 4\frac{2}{5} =$

2) $1\frac{3}{8} \div 1\frac{1}{4} =$

3) $6\frac{2}{5} \div 2\frac{4}{5} =$

4) $7\frac{1}{3} \div 6\frac{3}{4} =$

5) $7\frac{2}{5} \div 3\frac{3}{4} =$

6) $2\frac{4}{5} \div 3\frac{2}{3} =$

7) $8\frac{3}{5} \div 4\frac{3}{4} =$

8) $6\frac{3}{4} \div 2\frac{2}{9} =$

9) $5\frac{2}{7} \div 2\frac{2}{9} =$

10) $2\frac{2}{5} \div 3\frac{3}{5} =$

11) $4\frac{3}{7} \div 1\frac{7}{8} =$

12) $2\frac{5}{7} \div 2\frac{4}{5} =$

13) $8\frac{3}{5} \div 6\frac{1}{5} =$

14) $2\frac{5}{8} \div 1\frac{8}{9} =$

15) $5\frac{6}{7} \div 2\frac{3}{4} =$

16) $1\frac{3}{5} \div 2\frac{3}{8} =$

17) $5\frac{3}{4} \div 3\frac{2}{5} =$

18) $2\frac{3}{4} \div 3\frac{1}{5} =$

19) $3\frac{2}{3} \div 1\frac{2}{5} =$

20) $4\frac{1}{4} \div 2\frac{2}{3} =$

21) $3\frac{5}{6} \div 2\frac{4}{5} =$

22) $2\frac{1}{8} \div 1\frac{3}{4} =$

23) $5\frac{1}{2} \div 4\frac{2}{5} =$

24) $6\frac{3}{7} \div 2\frac{1}{7} =$

25) $3\frac{3}{6} \div 1\frac{5}{7} =$

26) $4\frac{4}{9} \div 4\frac{2}{3} =$

Answers – Chapter 1

Simplifying Fractions

1) $\frac{1}{2}$

2) $\frac{4}{5}$

3) $\frac{3}{4}$

4) $\frac{1}{4}$

5) $\frac{3}{4}$

6) $\frac{2}{3}$

7) $\frac{4}{5}$

8) $\frac{1}{4}$

9) $\frac{1}{2}$

10) $\frac{1}{7}$

11) $\frac{1}{3}$

12) $\frac{3}{4}$

13) $\frac{9}{11}$

14) $\frac{9}{10}$

15) $\frac{1}{3}$

16) $\frac{5}{14}$

17) $\frac{2}{5}$

18) $\frac{2}{3}$

19) $\frac{7}{16}$

20) $\frac{3}{4}$

21) $\frac{4}{5}$

22) B

23) A

24) B

Adding and Subtracting Fractions

1) $\frac{3}{3} = 1$

2) $\frac{5}{6}$

3) $\frac{9}{10}$

4) $\frac{23}{21}$

5) $\frac{23}{20}$

6) $\frac{4}{5}$

7) $\frac{19}{18}$

8) $\frac{39}{40}$

9) $\frac{62}{63}$

10) $\frac{31}{44}$

11) $\frac{25}{42}$

12) $\frac{27}{28}$

13) $\frac{1}{6}$

14) $\frac{2}{15}$

15) $\frac{1}{2}$

16) $\frac{1}{10}$

17) $\frac{22}{45}$

18) $\frac{29}{63}$

19) $\frac{3}{20}$

20) $\frac{7}{24}$

21) $\frac{1}{6}$

22) $\frac{3}{20}$

23) $\frac{1}{12}$

24) $\frac{3}{16}$

25) $\frac{1}{35}$

26) $\frac{7}{18}$

27) $\frac{3}{10}$

28) $\frac{7}{36}$

29) $-\frac{25}{91}$

30) $-\frac{23}{88}$

Multiplying and Dividing Fractions

1) $\frac{3}{8}$

2) $\frac{2}{5}$

3) $\frac{1}{10}$

4) $\frac{2}{15}$

5) $\frac{1}{20}$

6) $\frac{1}{5}$

7) $\frac{7}{27}$

8) $\frac{15}{56}$

9) $\frac{16}{21}$

Effortless
Math
Education

10) $\frac{1}{2}$

11) $\frac{1}{24}$

12) $\frac{1}{28}$

13) 2

14) $\frac{2}{3}$

15) $\frac{6}{5}$

16) $\frac{3}{8}$

17) $\frac{2}{3}$

18) $\frac{6}{7}$

19) $\frac{27}{25}$

20) $\frac{9}{23}$

21) $\frac{16}{13}$

22) $\frac{3}{2}$

23) $\frac{4}{3}$

24) $\frac{22}{63}$

25) $\frac{8}{15}$

26) $\frac{10}{11}$

27) $\frac{16}{75}$

28) $\frac{3}{4}$

29) $\frac{28}{15}$

30) $\frac{10}{33}$

Adding Mixed Numbers

1) $3\frac{3}{5}$

2) $6\frac{1}{3}$

3) $5\frac{1}{10}$

4) $5\frac{17}{30}$

5) $3\frac{7}{30}$

6) $4\frac{59}{63}$

7) $5\frac{23}{24}$

8) $5\frac{5}{63}$

9) $3\frac{29}{36}$

10) $6\frac{11}{18}$

11) $4\frac{1}{2}$

12) $5\frac{1}{10}$

13) $5\frac{5}{12}$

14) $6\frac{13}{22}$

15) $5\frac{5}{7}$

16) $5\frac{2}{3}$

17) $5\frac{16}{25}$

18) $5\frac{4}{15}$

19) $8\frac{4}{21}$

20) $5\frac{7}{8}$

21) $4\frac{17}{21}$

22) $5\frac{29}{30}$

23) $4\frac{29}{56}$

24) $5\frac{11}{12}$

25) $3\frac{43}{52}$

26) $5\frac{27}{35}$

Subtracting Mixed Numbers

1) $3\frac{1}{9}$

2) $3\frac{20}{21}$

3) $2\frac{5}{8}$

4) $4\frac{3}{10}$

5) $2\frac{11}{21}$

6) $1\frac{3}{4}$

7) $1\frac{31}{72}$

8) $2\frac{22}{63}$

9) $1\frac{5}{24}$

10) $2\frac{11}{36}$

11) $4\frac{11}{18}$

12) $1\frac{13}{24}$

13) $1\frac{1}{8}$

14) $2\frac{5}{16}$

15) $2\frac{8}{15}$

16) $1\frac{13}{34}$

17) $3\frac{11}{21}$

18) $1\frac{1}{3}$

19) $2\frac{1}{6}$

20) $2\frac{11}{18}$

21) $4\frac{13}{63}$

22) $1\frac{13}{35}$

23) $4\frac{2}{21}$

24) $2\frac{11}{18}$

25) $2\frac{2}{7}$

26) $4\frac{5}{16}$

Multiplying Mixed Numbers

1) $1\frac{2}{3}$

2) $11\frac{5}{8}$

3) $4\frac{4}{21}$

4) $10\frac{11}{16}$

5) $8\frac{1}{2}$

6) $23\frac{1}{3}$

7) $20\frac{7}{12}$

8) $22\frac{23}{40}$

9) $17\frac{11}{15}$

10) $12\frac{4}{21}$

11) $23\frac{3}{4}$

12) $14\frac{13}{27}$

13) $18\frac{5}{12}$

14) $36\frac{2}{5}$

15) $17\frac{17}{24}$

16) $14\frac{22}{35}$

17) $18\frac{5}{24}$

18) $16\frac{1}{4}$

19) $30\frac{2}{5}$

20) $11\frac{3}{8}$

21) $21\frac{8}{15}$

22) $13\frac{1}{7}$

23) $18\frac{2}{3}$

24) 30

25) $5\frac{31}{40}$

26) $30\frac{2}{3}$

Dividing Mixed Numbers

1) $1\frac{21}{44}$

2) $1\frac{1}{10}$

3) $2\frac{2}{7}$

4) $1\frac{7}{81}$

5) $1\frac{73}{75}$

6) $\frac{42}{55}$

7) $1\frac{77}{95}$

8) $3\frac{3}{80}$

9) $2\frac{53}{140}$

10) $\frac{2}{3}$

11) $2\frac{38}{105}$

12) $\frac{95}{98}$

13) $1\frac{12}{31}$

14) $1\frac{53}{136}$

15) $2\frac{10}{77}$

16) $\frac{64}{95}$

17) $1\frac{47}{68}$

18) $\frac{55}{64}$

19) $2\frac{13}{21}$

20) $1\frac{19}{32}$

21) $1\frac{31}{84}$

22) $1\frac{3}{14}$

23) $1\frac{1}{4}$

24) 3

25) $2\frac{1}{24}$

26) $\frac{20}{21}$

**Effortless
Math
Education**

Chapter 2: Decimal

Math Topics that you'll learn in this Chapter:

- ✓ Comparing Decimals
- ✓ Rounding Decimals
- ✓ Adding and Subtracting Decimals
- ✓ Multiplying and Dividing Decimals

Comparing Decimals

✍ *Write the correct comparison symbol (>, < or =).*

1) 0.50 ☐ 0.050

2) 0.025 ☐ 0.25

3) 2.060 ☐ 2.07

4) 1.75 ☐ 1.07

5) 4.04 ☐ 0.440

6) 3.05 ☐ 3.5

7) 5.05 ☐ 5.050

8) 1.02 ☐ 1.1

9) 2.45 ☐ 2.125

10) 0.932 ☐ 0.0932

11) 3.15 ☐ 3.150

12) 0.718 ☐ 0.89

13) 7.060 ☐ 7.60

14) 3.59 ☐ 3.129

15) 4.33 ☐ 4.319

16) 2.25 ☐ 2.250

17) 1.95 ☐ 1.095

18) 8.051 ☐ 8.50

19) 1.022 ☐ 1.020

20) 3.77 ☐ 3.770

Rounding Decimals

 Round each decimal to the nearest whole number.

1) 23.18   3) 14.45   5) 3.95

2) 8.6   4) 7.5   6) 56.7

 Round each decimal to the nearest tenth.

7) 22.652   9) 47.847   11) 16.184

8) 30.342   10) 82.88   12) 71.79

 Round each decimal to the nearest hundredth.

13) 5.439   15) 26.1855   17) 91.448

14) 12.907   16) 48.623   18) 29.354

 Round each decimal to the nearest thousandth.

19) 14.67374   21) 78.7191   23) 10.0678

20) 7.54647   22) 70.2732   24) 46.54765

Find more at
bit.ly/3mKEluf

Adding and Subtracting Decimals

✏️ *Add and subtract decimals.*

1)
$$31.13 - 11.45$$

2)
$$35.25 + 24.47$$

3)
$$73.50 + 22.78$$

4)
$$56.67 - 44.39$$

5)
$$71.47 + 16.25$$

6)
$$68.99 - 53.61$$

7)
$$66.24 - 23.11$$

8)
$$39.75 + 12.85$$

9)
$$229.25 - 84.67$$

✏️ *Find the missing number.*

10) ___ $+ 2.5 = 3.9$

11) $1.7 +$ ___ $= 4.98$

12) $5.25 +$ ___ $= 7$

13) $6.55 -$ ___ $= 2.45$

14) ___ $- 3.98 = 5.32$

15) ___ $- 11.67 = 14.48$

16) $12.35 +$ ___ $= 14.78$

17) ___ $- 23.89 = 13.90$

18) ___ $+ 17.28 = 19.56$

19) $77.90 +$ ___ $= 102.60$

Multiplying and Dividing Decimals

✎ *Find the product.*

1) $0.5 \times 0.4 =$

2) $2.5 \times 0.2 =$

3) $1.25 \times 0.5 =$

4) $0.75 \times 0.2 =$

5) $1.92 \times 0.8 =$

6) $0.55 \times 0.4 =$

7) $3.24 \times 1.2 =$

8) $12.5 \times 4.2 =$

9) $22.6 \times 8.2 =$

10) $17.2 \times 4.5 =$

11) $25.1 \times 12.5 =$

12) $33.2 \times 2.2 =$

✎ *Find the quotient.*

13) $1.67 \div 100 =$

14) $52.2 \div 1{,}000 =$

15) $4.2 \div 2 =$

16) $8.6 \div 0.5 =$

17) $12.6 \div 0.2 =$

18) $16.5 \div 5 =$

19) $13.25 \div 100 =$

20) $25.6 \div 0.4 =$

21) $28.24 \div 0.1 =$

22) $34.16 \div 0.25 =$

23) $44.28 \div 0.5 =$

24) $38.78 \div 0.02 =$

bit.ly/34DZ0cS

Find more at

Answers – Chapter 2

Comparing Decimals

1) >
2) <
3) <
4) >
5) >
6) <
7) =

8) <
9) >
10) >
11) =
12) <
13) <
14) >

15) >
16) =
17) >
18) <
19) >
20) =

Rounding Decimals

1) 23
2) 9
3) 14
4) 8
5) 4
6) 57
7) 22.7
8) 30.3

9) 47.8
10) 82.9
11) 16.2
12) 71.8
13) 5.44
14) 12.91
15) 26.19
16) 48.62

17) 91.45
18) 29.35
19) 14.674
20) 7.546
21) 78.719
22) 70.273
23) 10.068
24) 46.548

Adding and Subtracting Decimals

1) 19.68
2) 59.72
3) 96.28
4) 12.28
5) 87.72
6) 15.38
7) 43.13

8) 52.60
9) 144.58
10) 1.4
11) 3.28
12) 1.75
13) 4.1
14) 9.3

15) 26.15
16) 2.43
17) 37.79
18) 2.28
19) 24.7

Multiplying and Dividing Decimals

1) 0.2
2) 0.5
3) 0.625
4) 0.15
5) 1.536
6) 0.22
7) 3.888
8) 52.5
9) 185.32

10) 77.4
11) 313.75
12) 73.04
13) 0.0167
14) 0.0522
15) 2.1
16) 17.2
17) 63
18) 3.3

19) 0.1325
20) 64
21) 282.4
22) 136.64
23) 88.56
24) 1,939

Effortless
Math
Education

Chapter 3: Integers and Order of Operations

Math Topics that you'll learn in this Chapter:

- ✓ Adding and Subtracting Integers
- ✓ Multiplying and Dividing Integers
- ✓ Order of Operations
- ✓ Integers and Absolute Value

Adding and Subtracting Integers

✎ *Find each sum.*

1) $12 + (-5) =$

2) $(-14) + (-18) =$

3) $8 + (-28) =$

4) $43 + (-12) =$

5) $(-7) + (-11) + 4 =$

6) $37 + (-16) + 12 =$

7) $29 + (-21) + (-12) + 20 =$

8) $(-15) + (-25) + 18 + 25 =$

9) $30 + (-28) + (35 - 32) =$

10) $25 + (-15) + (44 - 17) =$

✎ *Find each difference.*

11) $(-12) - (-8) =$

12) $15 - (-20) =$

13) $(-11) - 25 =$

14) $30 - (-16) =$

15) $56 - (45 - 23) =$

16) $15 - (-4) - (-34) =$

17) $(24 + 14) - (-55) =$

18) $23 - 15 - (-3) =$

19) $49 - (15 + 12) - (-4) =$

20) $29 - (-17) - (-25) =$

21) $12 - (-8) - (-18) =$

22) $(15 - 28) - (-22) =$

23) $19 - 44 - (-14) =$

24) $67 - (57 + 19) - (-8) =$

25) $56 - (-12) + (-19) =$

26) $22 - (-44) + (-55) =$

Multiplying and Dividing Integers

✎ **Find each product.**

1) $(-7) \times (-8) =$

2) $(-4) \times 5 =$

3) $5 \times (-11) =$

4) $(-5) \times (-20) =$

5) $-(2) \times (-8) \times 3 =$

6) $(12 - 4) \times (-10) =$

7) $14 \times (-10) \times (-5) =$

8) $(18 + 12) \times (-8) =$

9) $9 \times (-15 + 6) \times 3 =$

10) $(-5) \times (-8) \times (-12) =$

✎ **Find each quotient.**

11) $16 \div (-4) =$

12) $(-25) \div (-5) =$

13) $(-40) \div (-8) =$

14) $64 \div (-8) =$

15) $(-49) \div 7 =$

16) $(-112) \div (-4) =$

17) $168 \div (-12) =$

18) $(-121) \div (-11) =$

19) $216 \div (-12) =$

20) $-(152) \div (8) =$

21) $(-152) \div (-8) =$

22) $-216 \div (-12) =$

23) $(-198) \div (-9) =$

24) $195 \div (-13) =$

25) $-(182) \div (-7) =$

26) $(126) \div (-14) =$

Order of Operations

✎ *Evaluate each expression.*

1) $5 + (4 \times 2) =$

2) $13 - (2 \times 5) =$

3) $(16 \times 2) + 18 =$

4) $(12 - 5) - (4 \times 3) =$

5) $25 + (14 \div 2) =$

6) $(18 \times 5) \div 5 =$

7) $(48 \div 2) \times (-4) =$

8) $(7 \times 5) + (25 - 12) =$

9) $64 + (3 \times 2) + 8 =$

10) $(20 \times 5) \div (4 + 1) =$

11) $(-9) + (12 \times 6) + 15 =$

12) $(7 \times 8) - (56 \div 4) =$

13) $(4 \times 8 \div 2) - (17 + 11) =$

14) $(18 + 8 - 15) \times 5 - 3 =$

15) $(25 - 12 + 45) \times (95 \div 5) =$

16) $28 + \big(15 - (32 \div 2)\big) =$

17) $(6 + 7 - 4 - 9) + (18 \div 2) =$

18) $(95 - 17) + (10 - 25 + 9) =$

19) $(18 \times 2) + (15 \times 5) - 12 =$

20) $12 + 8 - (42 \times 4) + 50 =$

Integers and Absolute Value

✍ *Write absolute value of each number.*

1) $|-7| =$

2) $|-11| =$

3) $|-9| =$

4) $|8| =$

5) $|4| =$

6) $|-18| =$

7) $|6| =$

8) $|0| =$

9) $|16| =$

10) $|-2| =$

11) $|-12|$

12) $|10| =$

13) $|3| =$

14) $|7| =$

15) $|-15| =$

16) $|-13| =$

17) $|19| =$

18) $|-12| =$

19) $|4| =$

20) $|-25| =$

✍ *Evaluate the value.*

21) $|-2| - \frac{|-10|}{2} =$

22) $8 - |2 - 14| - |-2| =$

23) $\frac{|-36|}{6} \times |-6| =$

24) $\frac{|5 \times -3|}{5} \times \frac{|-20|}{4} =$

25) $|2 \times -4| + \frac{|-40|}{5} =$

26) $\frac{|-28|}{4} \times \frac{|-55|}{11} =$

27) $|-12 + 4| \times \frac{|-4 \times 5|}{2}$

28) $\frac{|-10 \times 3|}{2} \times |-12| =$

Answers – Chapter 3

Adding and Subtracting Integers

1) 7
2) −32
3) −20
4) 31
5) −14
6) 33
7) 16
8) 3
9) 5

10) 37
11) −4
12) 35
13) −36
14) 46
15) 34
16) 53
17) 93
18) 11

19) 26
20) 71
21) 38
22) 9
23) −11
24) −1
25) 49
26) 11

Multiplying and Dividing Integers

1) 56
2) −20
3) −55
4) 100
5) 48
6) −80
7) 700
8) −240
9) −243

10) −480
11) −4
12) 5
13) 5
14) −8
15) −7
16) 28
17) −14
18) 11

19) −18
20) −19
21) 19
22) 18
23) 22
24) −15
25) 26
26) −9

Order of Operations

1) 13
2) 3
3) 50
4) −5
5) 32
6) 18
7) −96

8) 48
9) 78
10) 20
11) 78
12) 42
13) −12
14) 52

15) 1,102
16) 27
17) 9
18) 72
19) 99
20) −98

Effortless
Math
Education

Integers and Absolute Value

1) 7
2) 11
3) 9
4) 8
5) 4
6) 18
7) 6
8) 0
9) 16
10) 2

11) 12
12) 10
13) 3
14) 7
15) 15
16) 13
17) 19
18) 12
19) 4
20) 25

21) −3
22) −6
23) 36
24) 15
25) 16
26) 35
27) 80
28) 180

Effortless
Math
Education

Chapter 4: Ratios and Proportions

Math Topics that you'll learn in this Chapter:

- ✓ Simplifying Ratios
- ✓ Proportional Ratios
- ✓ Create Proportion
- ✓ Similarity and Ratios
- ✓ Simple Interest

27

Simplifying Ratios

✎ *Reduce each ratio.*

1) $12:8 =$ ___ : ___

2) $2:20 =$ ___ : ___

3) $3:36 =$ ___ : ___

4) $8:16 =$ ___ : ___

5) $6:100 =$ ___ : ___

6) $10:60 =$ ___ : ___

7) $21:49 =$ ___ : ___

8) $20:40 =$ ___ : ___

9) $10:50 =$ ___ : ___

10) $14:18 =$ ___ : ___

11) $45:27 =$ ___ : ___

12) $49:21 =$ ___ : ___

13) $100:10 =$ ___ : ___

14) $35:45 =$ ___ : ___

15) $8:20 =$ ___ : ___

16) $25:35 =$ ___ : ___

17) $21:27 =$ ___ : ___

18) $52:82 =$ ___ : ___

19) $12:36 =$ ___ : ___

20) $24:3 =$ ___ : ___

21) $15:30 =$ ___ : ___

22) $14:63 =$ ___ : ___

23) $68:80 =$ ___ : ___

24) $8:80 =$ ___ : ___

✎ *Write each ratio as a fraction in simplest form.*

25) $2:4 =$

26) $6:20 =$

27) $5:35 =$

28) $10:55 =$

29) $8:24 =$

30) $9:42 =$

31) $12:48 =$

32) $6:40 =$

33) $15:36 =$

34) $18:82 =$

35) $22:26 =$

36) $8:36 =$

37) $16:128 =$

38) $14:77 =$

39) $12:180 =$

40) $36:108 =$

41) $24:42 =$

42) $18:120 =$

43) $44:82 =$

44) $60:240 =$

45) $36:180 =$

Proportional Ratios

✏️ *Fill in the blanks; solve each proportion.*

1) $3 : 7 \quad = \quad \underline{} : 49$

2) $1 : 2 \quad = \quad 20 : \underline{}$

3) $1 : 5 \quad = \quad \underline{} : 50$

4) $7 : 9 \quad = \quad 14 : \underline{}$

5) $5 : 3 \quad = \quad 45 : \underline{}$

6) $7 : 3 \quad = \quad \underline{} : 18$

7) $10 : 1 \quad = \quad \underline{} : 10$

8) $1 : 3 \quad = \quad \underline{} : 27$

9) $8 : 1 \quad = \quad \underline{} : 8$

10) $9 : 2 \quad = \quad \underline{} : 14$

11) $3 : 12 \quad = \quad 12 : \underline{}$

12) $6 : 4 \quad = \quad 24 : \underline{}$

✏️ *State if each pair of ratios form a proportion.*

13) $\frac{3}{10}$ and $\frac{9}{30}$

14) $\frac{1}{2}$ and $\frac{16}{32}$

15) $\frac{5}{6}$ and $\frac{35}{42}$

16) $\frac{3}{7}$ and $\frac{27}{72}$

17) $\frac{2}{5}$ and $\frac{16}{45}$

18) $\frac{4}{9}$ and $\frac{40}{81}$

19) $\frac{6}{11}$ and $\frac{42}{77}$

20) $\frac{1}{6}$ and $\frac{8}{48}$

21) $\frac{6}{17}$ and $\frac{36}{85}$

22) $\frac{2}{7}$ and $\frac{24}{86}$

23) $\frac{12}{19}$ and $\frac{156}{247}$

24) $\frac{13}{21}$ and $\frac{182}{294}$

✏️ *Solve each proportion.*

25) $\frac{2}{5} = \frac{14}{x}, x = \underline{}$

26) $\frac{1}{6} = \frac{7}{x}, x = \underline{}$

27) $\frac{3}{5} = \frac{27}{x}, x = \underline{}$

28) $\frac{1}{5} = \frac{x}{80}, x = \underline{}$

29) $\frac{3}{7} = \frac{x}{63}, x = \underline{}$

30) $\frac{1}{4} = \frac{13}{x}, x = \underline{}$

31) $\frac{7}{9} = \frac{56}{x}, x = \underline{}$

32) $\frac{6}{11} = \frac{42}{x}, x = \underline{}$

33) $\frac{4}{7} = \frac{x}{77}, x = \underline{}$

34) $\frac{5}{13} = \frac{x}{143}, x = \underline{}$

35) $\frac{7}{19} = \frac{x}{209}, x = \underline{}$

36) $\frac{3}{13} = \frac{x}{195}, x = \underline{}$

bit.ly/37GHQxp

Find more at

Create Proportion

✐ **State if each pair of ratios form a proportion.**

1) $\frac{3}{8}$ and $\frac{24}{50}$

2) $\frac{3}{11}$ and $\frac{6}{22}$

3) $\frac{4}{5}$ and $\frac{16}{20}$

4) $\frac{5}{11}$ and $\frac{12}{33}$

5) $\frac{5}{10}$ and $\frac{15}{30}$

6) $\frac{4}{13}$ and $\frac{8}{24}$

7) $\frac{6}{9}$ and $\frac{24}{36}$

8) $\frac{7}{12}$ and $\frac{14}{20}$

9) $\frac{3}{8}$ and $\frac{27}{72}$

10) $\frac{12}{20}$ and $\frac{36}{60}$

11) $\frac{11}{12}$ and $\frac{55}{60}$

12) $\frac{12}{15}$ and $\frac{24}{25}$

13) $\frac{15}{19}$ and $\frac{20}{38}$

14) $\frac{10}{14}$ and $\frac{40}{56}$

15) $\frac{11}{13}$ and $\frac{44}{39}$

16) $\frac{15}{16}$ and $\frac{30}{32}$

17) $\frac{17}{19}$ and $\frac{34}{48}$

18) $\frac{5}{18}$ and $\frac{15}{54}$

19) $\frac{3}{14}$ and $\frac{18}{42}$

20) $\frac{7}{11}$ and $\frac{14}{32}$

21) $\frac{8}{11}$ and $\frac{32}{44}$

22) $\frac{8}{14}$ and $\frac{24}{54}$

✐ **Solve.**

23) The ratio of boys to girls in a class is $3:4$. If there are 27 boys in the class, how many girls are in that class? _____

24) The ratio of red marbles to blue marbles in a bag is $5:6$. If there are 66 marbles in the bag, how many of the marbles are red? _____

25) You can buy 6 cans of green beans at a supermarket for $3.60. How much does it cost to buy 48 cans of green beans? _____

Similarity and Ratios

✎ *Each pair of figures is similar. Find the missing side.*

1)

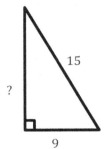

2)

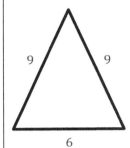

3)

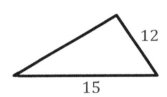

4)

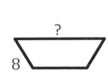

✎ **Solve.**

5) Two rectangles are similar. The first is 6 feet wide and 20 feet long. The second is 15 feet wide. What is the length of the second rectangle? _____

6) Two rectangles are similar. One is 2.5 meters by 9 meters. The longer side of the second rectangle is 22.5 meters. What is the other side of the second rectangle? _____

7) A building casts a shadow 24 ft long. At the same time a girl 5 ft tall casts a shadow 2 ft long. How tall is the building? _____

8) The scale of a map of Texas is 2 inches: 45 miles. If you measure the distance from Dallas to Martin County as 14.4 inches, approximately how far is Martin County from Dallas? _____

Simple Interest

✎ **Determine the simple interest for these loans.**

1) $450 at 7% for 2 years. $ _____
2) $5,200 at 4% for 3 years. $ _____
3) $1,300 at 5% for 6 years. $ _____
4) $5,400 at 3.5% for 6 months. $ _____
5) $600 at 4% for 9 months. $ _____

6) $24,000 at 5.5% for 5 years. $ _____
7) $15,600 at 3% for 2 years. $ _____
8) $1,200 at 5.5% for 4 years. $ _____
9) $1,600 at 4.5% for 9 months. $ _____
10) $12,000 at 2.2% for 5 years. $ _____

✎ **Solve each simple interest word problem.**

11) A new car, valued at $28,000, depreciates at 9% per year. What is the value of the car one year after purchase? $_____

12) Sara puts $4,000 into an investment yielding 5% annual simple interest; she left the money in for five years. How much interest does Sara get at the end of those five years? $_____

13) A bank is offering 3.5% simple interest on a savings account. If you deposit $7,500, how much interest will you earn in two years? $_____

14) $400 interest is earned on a principal of $2,000 at a simple interest rate of 5% interest per year. For how many years was the principal invested? _____

15) In how many years will $1,200 yield an interest of $180 at 3% simple interest? _____

16) Jim invested $4,000 in a bond at a yearly rate of 4.5%. He earned $540 in interest. How long was the money invested? _____

Answers – Chapter 4

Simplifying Ratios

1) $3:2$
2) $1:10$
3) $1:12$
4) $1:2$
5) $3:50$
6) $1:6$
7) $3:7$
8) $1:2$
9) $1:5$
10) $7:9$
11) $5:3$
12) $7:3$
13) $10:1$
14) $7:9$
15) $2:5$
16) $5:7$
17) $7:9$
18) $26:41$

19) $1:3$
20) $8:1$
21) $1:2$
22) $2:9$
23) $17:20$
24) $1:10$
25) $\frac{1}{2}$
26) $\frac{3}{10}$
27) $\frac{1}{7}$
28) $\frac{2}{11}$
29) $\frac{1}{3}$
30) $\frac{3}{14}$
31) $\frac{1}{4}$
32) $\frac{3}{20}$

33) $\frac{5}{12}$
34) $\frac{9}{41}$
35) $\frac{11}{13}$
36) $\frac{2}{9}$
37) $\frac{1}{8}$
38) $\frac{2}{11}$
39) $\frac{1}{15}$
40) $\frac{1}{3}$
41) $\frac{4}{7}$
42) $\frac{3}{20}$
43) $\frac{22}{41}$
44) $\frac{1}{4}$
45) $\frac{1}{5}$

Proportional Ratios

1) 21
2) 40
3) 10
4) 18
5) 27
6) 42
7) 100
8) 9
9) 64
10) 63
11) 48
12) 16

13) Yes
14) Yes
15) Yes
16) No
17) No
18) No
19) Yes
20) Yes
21) No
22) No
23) Yes
24) Yes

25) 35
26) 42
27) 45
28) 16
29) 27
30) 52
31) 72
32) 77
33) 44
34) 55
35) 77
36) 45

Effortless
Math
Education

Create Proportion

1) *No*	10) *Yes*	19) *No*
2) *Yes*	11) *Yes*	20) *No*
3) *Yes*	12) *No*	21) *Yes*
4) *No*	13) *No*	22) *No*
5) *Yes*	14) *Yes*	23) 36 *girls*
6) *No*	15) *No*	24) 30 *red marbles*
7) *Yes*	16) *Yes*	25) $28.80
8) *No*	17) *No*	
9) *Yes*	18) *Yes*	

Similarity and ratios

1) 12	4) 15	7) 60 feet
2) 2	5) 50 feet	8) 324 miles
3) 5	6) 6.25 meters	

Simple Interest

1) $63.00	7) $936.00	13) $525.00
2) $624.00	8) $264.00	14) 4 years
3) $390.00	9) $54.00	15) 5 years
4) $94.50	10) $1,320.00	16) 3 years
5) $18.00	11) $25,480.00	
6) $6,600.00	12) $1,000.00	

Chapter 5: Percentage

Math Topics that you'll learn in this Chapter:

- ✓ Percent Problems
- ✓ Percent of Increase and Decrease
- ✓ Discount, Tax and Tip

35

Percent Problems

✍ **Solve each problem.**

1) 20 is what percent of 50? ____%

2) 18 is what percent of 90? ____%

3) 12 is what percent of 15? ____%

4) 16 is what percent of 200? ____%

5) 24 is what percent of 800? ____%

6) 48 is what percent of 400? ____%

7) 90 is what percent of 750? ____%

8) 24 is what percent of 300? ____%

9) 60 is what percent of 400? ____%

10) 42 is what percent of 350? ___%

11) 11 is what percent of 44? ___%

12) 8 is what percent of 64? ___%

13) 210 is what percent of 875? ___%

14) 80 is what percent of 64? ___%

15) 15 is what percent of 12? ___%

16) 56 is what percent of 40? ___%

17) 36 is what percent of 240? ___%

18) 32 is what percent of 20? ___%

✍ **Solve each percent word problem.**

19) There are 48 employees in a company. On a certain day, 36 were present. What percent showed up for work? _____%

20) A metal bar weighs 24 ounces. 15% of the bar is gold. How many ounces of gold are in the bar? _____

21) A crew is made up of 12 women; the rest are men. If 20% of the crew are women, how many people are in the crew? _____

22) There are 48 students in a class and 6 of them are girls. What percent are boys? _____%

23) The Royals softball team played 75 games and won 60 of them. What percent of the games did they lose? _____%

Percent of Increase and Decrease

✎ *Find each percent of change.*

1) From 200 to 500.   ___ %

2) From 50 ft to 75 ft.   ___ %

3) From $250 to $350.   ___ %

4) From 60 cm to 90 cm. ___ %

5) From 30 to 90.   ___ %

6) From 30 to 6.   ___ %

7) From 80 to 120.   ___ %

8) From 800 to 200.   ___ %

9) From 25 to 15.   ___ %

10) From 32 to 8.   ___ %

✎ *Solve each percent of change word problem.*

11) Bob got a raise, and his hourly wage increased from $12 to $15. What is the percent increase? _____ %

12) The price of a pair of shoes increases from $20 to $32. What is the percent increase? ___ %

13) At a coffeeshop, the price of a cup of coffee increased from $1.20 to $1.44. What is the percent increase in the cost of the coffee? _____ %

14) 6 cm are cut from a 24 cm board. What is the percent decrease in length? _____ %

15) In a class, the number of students has been increased from 18 to 27. What is the percent increase? _____ %

16) The price of gasoline rose from $2.40 to $2.76 in one month. By what percent did the gas price rise? _____ %

17) A shirt was originally priced at $48. It went on sale for $38.40. What was the percent that the shirt was discounted? _____ %

bit.ly/3pgPQes

Find more at

Discount, Tax and Tip

Find the selling price of each item.

1) Original price of a computer: $500

   Tax: 6%   Selling price: $_____

2) Original price of a laptop: $350

   Tax: 8%   Selling price: $_____

3) Original price of a sofa: $800

   Tax: 7%   Selling price: $_____

4) Original price of a car: $18,500

   Tax: 8.5%   Selling price: $_____

5) Original price of a Table: $250

   Tax: 5%   Selling price: $_____

6) Original price of a house: $250,000

   Tax: 6.5%   Selling price: $_____

7) Original price of a tablet: $400

   Discount: 20%   Selling price: $_____

8) Original price of a chair: $150

   Discount: 15%   Selling price: $_____

9) Original price of a book: $50

   Discount: 25%   Selling price: $_____

10) Original price of a cellphone: $500

   Discount: 10%   Selling price: $_____

11) Food bill: $24

   Tip: 20%   Price: $_____

12) Food bill: $60

   Tipp: 15%   Price: $_____

13) Food bill: $32

   Tip: 20%   Price: $_____

14) Food bill: $18

   Tipp: 25%   Price: $_____

Solve each word problem.

15) Nicolas hired a moving company. The company charged $400 for its services, and Nicolas gives the movers a 15% tip. How much does Nicolas tip the movers? $_____

16) Mason has lunch at a restaurant and the cost of his meal is $30. Mason wants to leave a 20% tip. What is Mason's total bill including tip? $_____

17) The sales tax in Texas is 8.25% and an item costs $400. How much is the tax? $_____

18) The price of a table at Best Buy is $220. If the sales tax is 6%, what is the final price of the table including tax? $_____

Answers – Chapter 5

Percent Problems

1) 40%
2) 20%
3) 80%
4) 8%
5) 3%
6) 12%
7) 12%
8) 8%

9) 15%
10) 12%
11) 25%
12) 12.5%
13) 24%
14) 125%
15) 125%
16) 140%

17) 15%
18) 160%
19) 75%
20) 3.6 ounces
21) 60
22) 87.5%
23) 20%

Percent of Increase and Decrease

1) 150%
2) 50%
3) 40%
4) 50%
5) 200%
6) 80%

7) 50%
8) 75%
9) 40%
10) 75%
11) 25%
12) 60%

13) 20%
14) 25%
15) 50%
16) 15%
17) 20%

Discount, Tax and Tip

1) $530.00
2) $378.00
3) $856.00
4) $20,072.50
5) $262.50
6) $266,250

7) $320.00
8) $127.50
9) $37.50
10) $450.00
11) $28.80
12) $69.00

13) $38.40
14) $22.50
15) $60.00
16) $36.00
17) $33.00
18) $233.20

Effortless Math Education

Chapter 6: Expressions and Variables

Math Topics that you'll learn in this Chapter:

- ✓ Simplifying Variable Expressions
- ✓ Simplifying Polynomial Expressions
- ✓ Evaluating One Variable
- ✓ Evaluating Two Variables
- ✓ The Distributive Property

41

Simplifying Variable Expressions

🖎 *Simplify each expression.*

1) $3(x + 9) =$

2) $(-6)(8x - 4) =$

3) $7x + 3 - 3x =$

4) $-2 - x^2 - 6x^2 =$

5) $3 + 10x^2 + 2 =$

6) $8x^2 + 6x + 7x^2 =$

7) $5x^2 - 12x^2 + 8x =$

8) $2x^2 - 2x - x =$

9) $4x + 6(2 - 5x) =$

10) $10x + 8(10x - 6) =$

11) $9(-2x - 6) - 5 =$

12) $2x^2 + (-8x) =$

13) $x - 3 + 5 - 3x =$

14) $2 - 3x + 12 - 2x =$

15) $32x - 4 + 23 + 2x =$

16) $(-6)(8x - 4) + 10x =$

17) $14x - 5(5 - 8x) =$

18) $23x + 4(9x + 3) + 12 =$

19) $3(-7x + 5) + 20x =$

20) $12x - 3x(x + 9) =$

21) $7x + 5x(3 - 3x) =$

22) $5x(-8x + 12) + 14x =$

23) $40x + 12 + 2x^2 =$

24) $5x(x - 3) - 10 =$

25) $8x - 7 + 8x + 2x^2 =$

26) $2x^2 - 5x - 7x =$

27) $7x - 3x^2 - 5x^2 - 3 =$

28) $4 + x^2 - 6x^2 - 12x =$

29) $12x + 8x^2 + 2x + 20 =$

30) $2x^2 + 6x + 3x^2 =$

31) $23 + 15x^2 + 8x - 4x^2 =$

32) $8x - 12x - x^2 + 13 =$

Simplifying Polynomial Expressions

✎ *Simplify each polynomial.*

1) $(2x^3 + 5x^2) - (12x + 2x^2) =$ _____

2) $(2x^5 + 2x^3) - (7x^3 + 6x^2) =$ _____

3) $(12x^4 + 4x^2) - (2x^2 - 6x^4) =$ _____

4) $14x - 3x^2 - 2(6x^2 + 6x^3) =$ _____

5) $(5x^3 - 3) + 5(2x^2 - 3x^3) =$ _____

6) $(4x^3 - 2x) - 2(4x^3 - 2x^4) =$ _____

7) $2(4x - 3x^3) - 3(3x^3 + 4x^2) =$ _____

8) $(2x^2 - 2x) - (2x^3 + 5x^2) =$ _____

9) $2x^3 - (4x^4 + 2x) + x^2 =$ _____

10) $x^4 - 2(x^2 + x) + 3x =$ _____

11) $(2x^2 - x^4) - (4x^4 - x^2) =$ _____

12) $4x^2 - 5x^3 + 15x^4 - 12x^3 =$ _____

13) $2x^2 - 5x^4 + 14x^4 - 11x^3 =$ _____

14) $2x^2 + 5x^3 - 7x^2 + 12x =$ _____

15) $2x^4 - 5x^5 + 8x^4 - 8x^2 =$ _____

16) $5x^3 + 15x - x^2 - 2x^3 =$ _____

bit.ly/2WT5gtn

Find more at

Evaluating One Variable

✎ **Evaluate each expression using the value given.**

1) $5 + x$, $x = 2$

2) $x - 2$, $x = 4$

3) $8x + 1$, $x = 9$

4) $x - 12$, $x = -1$

5) $9 - x$, $x = 3$

6) $x + 2$, $x = 5$

7) $3x + 7$, $x = 6$

8) $x + (-5)$, $x = -2$

9) $3x + 6$, $x = 4$

10) $4x + 6$, $x = -1$

11) $10 + 2x - 6$, $x = 3$

12) $10 - 3x$, $x = 8$

13) $2x - 5$, $x = 4$

14) $5x + 6$, $x = -3$

15) $12x + 6$, $x = 2$

16) $10 - 3x$, $x = -2$

17) $5(6x + 2)$, $x = 8$

18) $2(-7x - 2)$, $x = 3$

19) $9x - 3x + 12$, $x = 6$

20) $(6x + 3) \div 5$, $x = 2$

21) $(x + 16) \div 3$, $x = 8$

22) $4x - 12 + 8x$, $x = -6$

23) $(16 - 12x)(-2)$, $x = -3$

24) $12x^2 + 5x - 3$, $x = 2$

25) $x^2 - 11x$, $x = -4$

26) $2x(6 - 4x)$, $x = 5$

27) $14x + 7 - 3x^2$, $x = -3$

28) $(-5)(10x - 20 + 2x)$, $x = 2$

29) $(-3) + \frac{x}{4} + 2x$, $x = 16$

30) $(-2) + \frac{x}{7}$, $x = 21$

31) $\left(-\frac{14}{x}\right) - 9 + 4x$, $x = 2$

32) $\left(-\frac{6}{x}\right) - 9 + 2x$, $x = 3$

Evaluating Two Variables

✎ *Evaluate each expression using the values given.*

1) $2x + 4y$,

   $x = 3, y = 2$

2) $8x + 5y$,

   $x = 1, y = 5$

3) $-2a + 4b$,

   $a = 6, b = 3$

4) $4x + 7 - 2y$,

   $x = 7, y = 6$

5) $5z + 12 - 4k$,

   $z = 5, k = 2$

6) $2(-x - 2y)$,

   $x = 6, y = 9$

7) $18a + 2b$,

   $a = 2, b = 8$

8) $4x \div 3y$,

   $x = 3, y = 2$

9) $2x + 15 + 4y$,

   $x = -2, y = 4$

10) $4a - (15 - b)$,

    $a = 4, b = 6$

11) $5z + 19 + 8k$,

    $z = -5, k = 4$

12) $xy + 12 + 5x$,

    $x = 7, y = 2$

13) $2x + 4y - 3 + 2$,

    $x = 5, y = 3$

14) $\left(-\frac{12}{x}\right) + 1 + 5y$,

    $x = 6, y = 8$

15) $(-4)(-2a - 2b)$,

    $a = 5, b = 3$

16) $10 + 3x + 7 - 2y$,

    $x = 7, y = 6$

17) $9x + 2 - 4y + 5$,

    $x = 7, y = 5$

18) $6 + 3(-2x - 3y)$,

    $x = 9, y = 7$

19) $2x + 14 + 4y$,

    $x = 6, y = 8$

20) $4a - (5a - b) + 5$,

    $a = 4, b = 6$

The Distributive Property

✎ **Use the distributive property to simply each expression.**

1) $2(2 + 3x) =$

2) $3(5 + 5x) =$

3) $4(3x - 8) =$

4) $(6x - 2)(-2) =$

5) $(-3)(x + 2) =$

6) $(2 + 2x)5 =$

7) $(-4)(4 - 2x) =$

8) $-(-2 - 5x) =$

9) $(-6x + 2)(-1) =$

10) $(-5)(x - 2) =$

11) $-(7 - 3x) =$

12) $8(8 + 2x) =$

13) $2(12 + 2x) =$

14) $(-6x + 8)4 =$

15) $(3 - 6x)(-7) =$

16) $(-12)(2x + 1) =$

17) $(8 - 2x)9 =$

18) $5(7 + 9x) =$

19) $11(5x + 2) =$

20) $(-4x + 6)6 =$

21) $(3 - 6x)(-8) =$

22) $(-12)(2x - 3) =$

23) $(10 - 2x)9 =$

24) $(-5)(11x - 2) =$

25) $(1 - 9x)(-10) =$

26) $(-6)(x + 8) =$

27) $(-4 + 3x)(-8) =$

28) $(-5)(1 - 11x) =$

29) $11(3x - 12) =$

30) $(-12x + 14)(-5) =$

31) $(-5)(4x - 1) + 4(x + 2) =$

32) $(-3)(x + 4) - (2 + 3x) =$

Answers – Chapter 6

Simplifying Variable Expressions

1) $3x + 27$
2) $-48x + 24$
3) $4x + 3$
4) $-7x^2 - 2$
5) $10x^2 + 5$
6) $15x^2 + 6x$
7) $-7x^2 + 8x$
8) $2x^2 - 3x$
9) $-26x + 12$
10) $90x - 48$

11) $-18x - 59$
12) $2x^2 - 8x$
13) $-2x + 2$
14) $-5x + 14$
15) $34x + 19$
16) $-38x + 24$
17) $54x - 25$
18) $59x + 24$
19) $-x + 15$
20) $-3x^2 - 15x$
21) $-15x^2 + 22x$

22) $-40x^2 + 74x$
23) $2x^2 + 40x + 12$
24) $5x^2 - 15x - 10$
25) $2x^2 + 16x - 7$
26) $2x^2 - 12x$
27) $-8x^2 + 7x - 3$
28) $-5x^2 - 12x + 4$
29) $8x^2 + 14x + 20$
30) $5x^2 + 6x$
31) $11x^2 + 8x + 23$
32) $-x^2 - 4x + 13$

Simplifying Polynomial Expressions

1) $2x^3 + 3x^2 - 12x$
2) $2x^5 - 5x^3 - 6x^2$
3) $18x^4 + 2x^2$
4) $-12x^3 - 15x^2 + 14x$
5) $-10x^3 + 10x^2 - 3$
6) $4x^4 - 4x^3 - 2x$
7) $-15x^3 - 12x^2 + 8x$
8) $-2x^3 - 3x^2 - 2x$

9) $-4x^4 + 2x^3 + x^2 - 2x$
10) $x^4 - 2x^2 + x$
11) $-5x^4 + 3x^2$
12) $15x^4 - 17x^3 + 4x^2$
13) $9x^4 - 11x^3 + 2x^2$
14) $5x^3 - 5x^2 + 12x$
15) $-5x^5 + 10x^4 - 8x^2$
16) $3x^3 - x^2 + 15x$

Evaluating One Variables

1) 7
2) 2
3) 73
4) -13
5) 6
6) 7
7) 25
8) -7
9) 18
10) 2
11) 10

12) -14
13) 3
14) -9
15) 30
16) 16
17) 250
18) -46
19) 48
20) 3
21) 8
22) -84

23) -104
24) 55
25) 60
26) -140
27) -62
28) -20
29) 33
30) 1
31) -8
32) -5

Evaluating Two Variables

1) 14
2) 33

3) 0
4) 23

5) 29
6) -48

Effortless Math Education

7) 52
8) 2
9) 27
10) 7
11) 26
12) 61

13) 21
14) 39
15) 64
16) 26
17) 50

18) −111
19) 58
20) 7

The Distributive Property

1) $6x + 4$
2) $15x + 15$
3) $12x − 32$
4) $−12x + 4$
5) $−3x − 6$
6) $10x + 10$
7) $8x − 16$
8) $5x + 2$
9) $6x − 2$
10) $−5x + 10$
11) $3x − 7$

12) $16x + 64$
13) $4x + 24$
14) $−24x + 32$
15) $42x − 21$
16) $−24x − 12$
17) $−18x + 72$
18) $45x + 35$
19) $55x + 22$
20) $−24x + 36$
21) $48x − 24$
22) $−24x + 36$

23) $−18x + 90$
24) $−55x + 10$
25) $90x − 10$
26) $−6x − 48$
27) $−24x + 32$
28) $55x − 5$
29) $33x − 132$
30) $60x − 70$
31) $−16x + 13$
32) $−6x − 14$

Chapter 7: Equations and Inequalities

Math Topics that you'll learn in this Chapter:

- ✓ One–Step Equations
- ✓ Multi–Step Equations
- ✓ System of Equations
- ✓ Graphing Single–Variable Inequalities
- ✓ One–Step Inequalities
- ✓ Multi–Step Inequalities

49

One-Step Equations

✎ *Solve each equation.*

1) $2x = 20, x =$ ____

2) $4x = 16, x =$ ____

3) $8x = 24, x =$ ____

4) $6x = 30, x =$ ____

5) $x + 5 = 8, x =$ ____

6) $x - 1 = 5, x =$ ____

7) $x - 8 = 3, x =$ ____

8) $x + 6 = 12, x =$ ____

9) $x - 2 = 17, x =$ ____

10) $8 = 12 + x, x =$ ____

11) $x - 5 = 4, x =$ ____

12) $2 - x = -12, x =$ ____

13) $16 = -4 + x, x =$ ____

14) $x - 4 = -25, x =$ ____

15) $x + 12 = -9, x =$ ____

16) $14 = 18 - x, x =$ ____

17) $2 + x = -14, x =$ ____

18) $x - 5 = 15, x =$ ____

19) $25 = x - 5, x =$ ____

20) $x - 3 = -12, x =$ ____

21) $x - 12 = 12, x =$ ____

22) $x - 12 = -25, x =$ ____

23) $x - 13 = 32, x =$ ____

24) $-55 = x - 18, x =$ ____

25) $x - 12 = 18, x =$ ____

26) $20 = 5x, x =$ ____

27) $x - 30 = 20, x =$ ____

28) $x - 12 = 32, x =$ ____

29) $36 - x = 3, x =$ ____

30) $x - 14 = 14, x =$ ____

31) $19 - x = -15, x =$ ____

32) $x - 19 = -35, x =$ ____

Multi–Step Equations

✒ *Solve each equation.*

1) $2x + 3 = 5$

2) $-x + 8 = 5$

3) $3x - 4 = 5$

4) $-(2 - x) = 5$

5) $2x - 18 = 12$

6) $4x - 2 = 6$

7) $2x - 14 = 4$

8) $5x + 10 = 25$

9) $8x + 9 = 25$

10) $-3(2 + x) = 3$

11) $-2(4 + x) = 4$

12) $20 = -(x - 8)$

13) $2(2 - 2x) = 20$

14) $-12 = -(2x + 8)$

15) $5(2 + x) = 5$

16) $2(x - 14) = 4$

17) $-28 = 2x + 12x$

18) $3x + 15 = -x - 5$

19) $2(3 + 2x) = -18$

20) $12 - 2x = -8 - x$

21) $10 - 3x = 14 + x$

22) $10 + 10x = -2 + 4x$

23) $24 = (-4x) - 8 + 8$

24) $12 = 2x - 12 + 6x$

25) $-12 = -4x - 6 + 2x$

26) $4x - 12 = -18 + 5x$

27) $5x - 10 = 2x + 5$

28) $-7 - 3x = 2(3 - 2x)$

29) $x - 2 = -3(6 - 3x)$

30) $10x - 56 = 12x - 114$

31) $4x - 8 = -4(11 + 2x)$

32) $-5x - 14 = 6x + 52$

Systems of Equations

✏️ *Solve each system of equations.*

1) $-2x + 2y = 4$ $x =$ ____
    $-2x + y = 3$ $y =$ ____

2) $-10x + 2y = -6$ $x =$ ____
    $6x - 16y = 48$ $y =$ ____

3) $y = -8$ $x =$ ____
    $16x - 12y = 32$

4) $2y = -6x + 10$ $x =$ ____
    $10x - 8y = -6$ $y =$ ____

5) $10x - 9y = -13$ $x =$ ____
    $-5x + 3y = 11$ $y =$ ____

6) $-3x - 4y = 5$ $x =$ ____
    $x - 2y = 5$ $y =$ ____

7) $5x - 14y = -23$ $x =$ ____
    $-6x + 7y = 8$ $y =$ ____

8) $10x - 14y = -4$ $x =$ ____
    $-10x - 20y = -30$ $y =$ ____

9) $-4x + 12y = 12$ $x =$ ____
    $-14x + 16y = -10$ $y =$ ____

10) $x + 20y = 56$ $x =$ ____
    $x + 15y = 41$ $y =$ ____

11) $6x - 7y = -8$ $x =$ ____
    $-x - 4y = -9$ $y =$ ____

12) $-3x + 2y = -18$ $x =$ ____
    $8x - 2y = 28$ $y =$ ____

13) $-5x + y = -3$ $x =$ ____
    $3x - 8y = 24$ $y =$ ____

14) $3x - 2y = 2$ $x =$ ____
    $5x - 5y = 10$ $y =$ ____

15) $8x + 14y = 4$ $x =$ ____
    $-6x - 7y = -10$ $y =$ ____

16) $10x + 7y = 1$ $x =$ ____
    $-5x - 7y = 24$ $y =$ ____

Graphing Single-Variable Inequalities

✎ *Draw a graph for each inequality.*

1) $x > 2$

2) $x < 5$

3) $x > -1$

4) $x < 3$

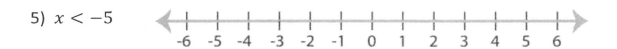

5) $x < -5$

6) $x > -2$

7) $x < 0$

8) $x > 4$

One-Step Inequalities

✎ *Solve each inequality and graph it.*

1) $x + 2 \geq 3$

```
-6  -5  -4  -3  -2  -1   0   1   2   3   4   5   6
```

2) $x - 1 \leq 2$

```
-6  -5  -4  -3  -2  -1   0   1   2   3   4   5   6
```

3) $2x \geq 12$

```
-6  -5  -4  -3  -2  -1   0   1   2   3   4   5   6
```

4) $4 + x \leq 5$

```
-6  -5  -4  -3  -2  -1   0   1   2   3   4   5   6
```

5) $x + 3 \leq -3$

```
-6  -5  -4  -3  -2  -1   0   1   2   3   4   5   6
```

6) $4x \geq 16$

```
-6  -5  -4  -3  -2  -1   0   1   2   3   4   5   6
```

7) $9x \leq 18$

```
-6  -5  -4  -3  -2  -1   0   1   2   3   4   5   6
```

8) $x + 2 \geq 7$

```
-6  -5  -4  -3  -2  -1   0   1   2   3   4   5   6
```

Multi-Step Inequalities

✏️ **Solve each inequality.**

1) $x - 2 \le 6$

2) $3 - x \le 3$

3) $2x - 4 \le 8$

4) $3x - 5 \ge 16$

5) $x - 5 \ge 10$

6) $2x - 8 \le 6$

7) $8x - 2 \le 14$

8) $-5 + 3x \le 10$

9) $2(x - 3) \le 6$

10) $7x - 5 \le 9$

11) $4x - 21 < 19$

12) $2x - 3 < 21$

13) $17 - 3x \ge -13$

14) $9 + 4x < 21$

15) $3 + 2x \ge 19$

16) $6 + 2x < 32$

17) $4x - 1 < 7$

18) $3(3 - 2x) \ge -15$

19) $-(3 + 4x) < 13$

20) $20 - 8x \ge -28$

21) $-3(x - 7) > 21$

22) $\dfrac{2x+6}{4} \le 10$

23) $\dfrac{4x+8}{2} \le 12$

24) $\dfrac{3x-8}{7} > 1$

25) $4 + \dfrac{x}{3} < 7$

26) $\dfrac{9x}{7} - 7 < 2$

27) $\dfrac{4x+12}{4} > 1$

28) $15 + \dfrac{x}{5} < 12$

Answers – Chapter 7

One–Step Equations

1) 10
2) 4
3) 3
4) 5
5) 3
6) 6
7) 11
8) 6
9) 19
10) −4
11) 9

12) 14
13) 20
14) −21
15) −21
16) 4
17) −16
18) 20
19) 30
20) −9
21) 24
22) −13

23) 45
24) −37
25) 30
26) 4
27) 50
28) 44
29) 33
30) 28
31) 34
32) −16

Multi–Step Equations

1) 1
2) 3
3) 3
4) 7
5) 15
6) 2
7) 9
8) 3
9) 2
10) −3
11) −6

12) −12
13) −4
14) 2
15) −1
16) 16
17) −2
18) −5
19) −6
20) 20
21) −1
22) −2

23) −6
24) 3
25) 3
26) 6
27) 5
28) 13
29) 2
30) 29
31) −3
32) −6

Systems of Equations

1) $x = -1, y = 1$
2) $x = 0, y = -3$
3) $x = -4$
4) $x = 1, y = 2$
5) $x = -4, y = -3$
6) $x = 1, y = -2$

7) $x = 1, y = 2$
8) $x = 1, y = 1$
9) $x = 3, y = 2$
10) $x = -4, y = 3$
11) $x = 1, y = 2$
12) $x = 2, y = -6$

13) $x = 0, y = -3$
14) $x = -2, y = -4$
15) $x = 4, y = -2$
16) $x = 5, y = -7$

Effortless
Math
Education

Graphing Single–Variable Inequalities

1)

2)

3)

4)

5)

6)

7)

8)

One–Step Inequalities

1)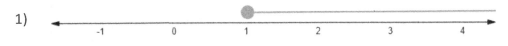

2)

3)

4)

Effortless
Math
Education

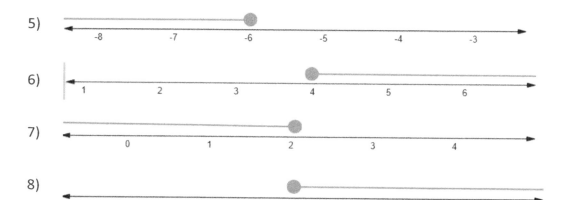

Multi-Step Inequalities

1) $x \le 8$
2) $x \ge 0$
3) $x \le 6$
4) $x \ge 7$
5) $x \ge 15$
6) $x \le 7$
7) $x \le 2$
8) $x \le 5$
9) $x \le 6$
10) $x \le 2$

11) $x < 10$
12) $x < 12$
13) $x \le 10$
14) $x < 3$
15) $x \ge 8$
16) $x < 13$
17) $x < 2$
18) $x \le 4$
19) $x > -4$
20) $x \le 6$

21) $x < 0$
22) $x \le 17$
23) $x \le 4$
24) $x > 5$
25) $x < 9$
26) $x < 7$
27) $x > -2$
28) $x < -15$

Chapter 8: Lines and Slope

Math Topics that you'll learn in this Chapter:

- ✓ Finding Slope
- ✓ Graphing Lines Using Slope–Intercept Form
- ✓ Writing Linear Equations
- ✓ Graphing Linear Inequalities
- ✓ Finding Midpoint
- ✓ Finding Distance of Two Points

Finding Slope

✍ **Find the slope of each line.**

1) $y = x - 1$

2) $y = -2x + 5$

3) $y = 2x - 1$

4) $y = -x - 8$

5) $y = 6 + 5x$

6) $y = 2 - 3x$

7) $y = 4x + 12$

8) $y = -6x + 2$

9) $y = -x + 8$

10) $y = 7x - 5$

11) $y = \frac{1}{2}x + 3$

12) $y = -\frac{2}{3}x + 1$

13) $-x + 2y = 5$

14) $2x + 2y = 6$

15) $8y - 2x = 10$

16) $5y - x = 2$

✍ **Find the slope of the line through each pair of points.**

17) $(1, 1), (2, 3)$

18) $(-1, 2), (0, 3)$

19) $(3, -1), (2, 3)$

20) $(-2, -1), (0, 5)$

21) $(5, 1), (2, 4)$

22) $(-3, 1), (-2, 4)$

23) $(6, 2), (7, 4)$

24) $(6, -5), (3, 4)$

25) $(12, -9), (11, -8)$

26) $(7, 4), (5, -2)$

27) $(1, 1), (3, 5)$

28) $(7, -12), (5, 10)$

Graphing Lines Using Slope–Intercept Form

✎ *Sketch the graph of each line.*

1) $y = 3x - 2$

2) $y = -x + 1$

3) $x + y = 4$

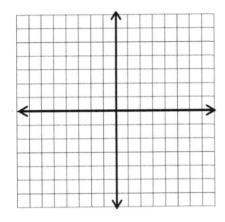

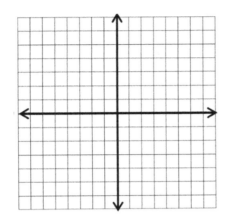

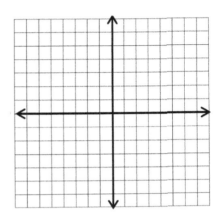

4) $x - y = -5$

5) $2x - y = -4$

6) $3x - 2y = -6$

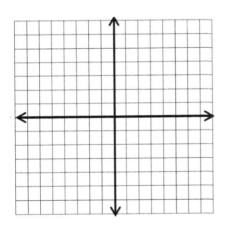

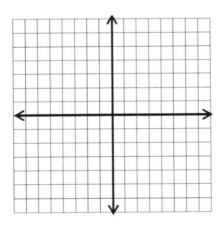

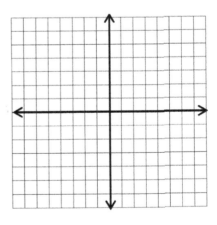

bit.ly/3hfdnJL

Find more at

Writing Linear Equations

✍ **Write the equation of the line through the given points.**

1) through: $(1, -2), (2, 3)$

2) through: $(-2, 1), (1, 4)$

3) through: $(-2, 1), (0, 5)$

4) through: $(5, 4), (2, 1)$

5) through: $(-4, 9), (3, 2)$

6) through: $(8, 3), (7, 2)$

7) through: $(7, -2), (5, 2)$

8) through: $(-3, 9), (5, -7)$

9) through: $(6, 8), (4, 14)$

10) through: $(5, 9), (7, -3)$

11) through: $(-2, 8), (-6, -4)$

12) through: $(3, 3), (1, -5)$

13) through: $(8, -5), (-5, 8)$

14) through: $(2, -6), (-1, 3)$

15) through: $(5, 5), (2, -4)$

16) through: $(-1, 8), (2, -7)$

✍ **Solve each problem.**

17) What is the equation of a line with slope 2 and intercept 4? _____

18) What is the equation of a line with slope 4 and intercept 12? _____

19) What is the equation of a line with slope 4 and passes through point $(4, 2)$?

_____

20) What is the equation of a line with slope -2 and passes through point $(-2, 4)$?

_____

21) The slope of a line is -3 and it passes through point $(-1, 5)$. What is the equation of the line? _____

22) The slope of a line is 3 and it passes through point $(-1, 4)$. What is the equation of the line? _____

Graphing Linear Inequalities

✎ *Sketch the graph of each linear inequality.*

1) $y > 3x - 1$

2) $y < -x + 4$

3) $y \leq -5x + 8$

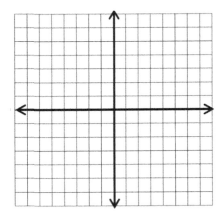
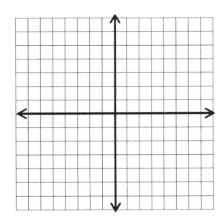
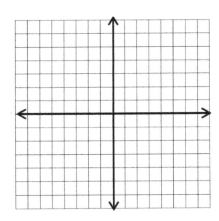

4) $2y \geq 8 + 6x$

5) $y < 2x - 3$

6) $4y \leq -6x + 2$

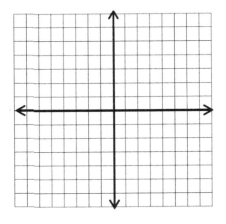
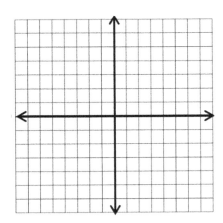
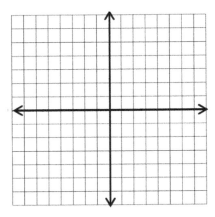

Finding Midpoint

 Find the midpoint of the line segment with the given endpoints.

1) $(-2, -2), (0, 2)$

2) $(5, 1), (-2, 4)$

3) $(4, -1), (0, 3)$

4) $(-3, 5), (-1, 3)$

5) $(3, -2), (7, -6)$

6) $(-4, -3), (2, -7)$

7) $(5, 0), (-5, 8)$

8) $(-6, 4), (-2, 0)$

9) $(-3, 4), (9, -6)$

10) $(2, 8), (6, -2)$

11) $(4, 7), (-6, 5)$

12) $(9, 3), (-1, -7)$

13) $(-4, 12), (-2, 6)$

14) $(14, 5), (8, -1)$

15) $(11, 7), (-3, 1)$

16) $(-7, -4), (-3, 8)$

17) $(13, 7), (5, 11)$

18) $(-5, -10), (9, -2)$

19) $(8, 15), (-2, 7)$

20) $(13, -2), (5, 10)$

21) $(2, -2), (3, -5)$

22) $(0, 2), (-2, -6)$

23) $(7, 4), (9, -1)$

24) $(4, -5), (0, 8)$

 Solve each problem.

25) One endpoint of a line segment is $(1, 2)$ and the midpoint of the line segment is $(-1, 4)$. What is the other endpoint? _____

26) One endpoint of a line segment is $(-3, 6)$ and the midpoint of the line segment is $(5, 2)$. What is the other endpoint? _____

27) One endpoint of a line segment is $(-2, -6)$ and the midpoint of the line segment is $(6, 8)$. What is the other endpoint? _____

Finding Distance of Two Points

✎ **Find the distance between each pair of points.**

1) $(2, 1), (-1, -3)$

2) $(-2, -1), (2, 2)$

3) $(-1, 0), (5, 8)$

4) $(-4, -1), (1, 11)$

5) $(3, -2), (-6, -14)$

6) $(-6, 0), (-2, 3)$

7) $(3, 2), (11, 17)$

8) $(-6, -10), (6, -1)$

9) $(5, 9), (-11, -3)$

10) $(9, -3), (3, -11)$

11) $(2, 0), (12, 24)$

12) $(8, 4), (3, -8)$

13) $(4, 2), (-5, -10)$

14) $(-5, 6), (3, 21)$

15) $(0, 8), (-4, 5)$

16) $(-8, -5), (4, 0)$

17) $(3, 5), (-5, -10)$

18) $(-2, 3), (22, 13)$

19) $(7, 2), (-8, -18)$

20) $(-5, 4), (7, 9)$

✎ **Solve each problem.**

21) Triangle ABC is a right triangle on the coordinate system and its vertices are $(-2, 5)$, $(-2, 1)$, and $(1, 1)$. What is the area of triangle ABC? _____

22) Three vertices of a triangle on a coordinate system are $(1, 1)$, $(1, 4)$, and $(5, 4)$. What is the perimeter of the triangle? _____

23) Four vertices of a rectangle on a coordinate system are $(2, 5)$, $(2, 2)$, $(6, 5)$, and $(6, 2)$. What is its perimeter? _____

Answers – Chapter 8

Finding Slope

1) 1	11) $\frac{1}{2}$	19) -4
2) -2	12) $-\frac{2}{3}$	20) 3
3) 2	13) $\frac{1}{2}$	21) -1
4) -1	14) -1	22) 3
5) 5	15) $\frac{1}{4}$	23) 2
6) -3	16) $\frac{1}{5}$	24) -3
7) 4	17) 2	25) -1
8) -6	18) 1	26) 3
9) -1		27) 2
10) 7		28) -11

Graphing Lines Using Slope–Intercept Form

1) $y = 3x - 2$ 2) $y = -x + 1$ 3) $x + y = 4$

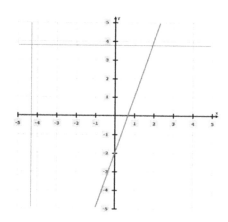
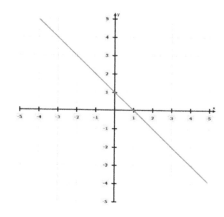
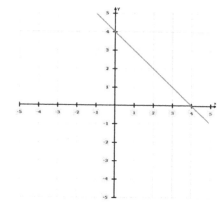

4) $x - y = -5$

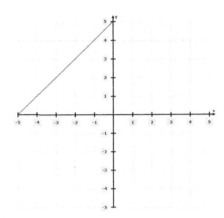

5) $2x - y = -4$

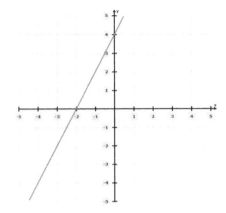

6) $3x - 2y = -6$

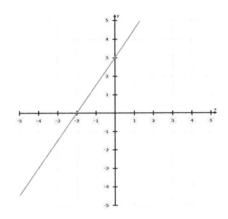

Writing Linear Equations

1) $y = 5x - 7$
2) $y = x + 3$
3) $y = 2x + 5$
4) $y = x - 1$
5) $y = -x + 5$
6) $y = x - 5$
7) $y = -2x + 12$
8) $y = -2x + 3$

9) $y = -3x + 26$
10) $y = -6x + 39$
11) $y = 3x + 14$
12) $y = 4x - 9$
13) $y = -x + 3$
14) $y = -3x$
15) $y = 3x - 10$
16) $y = -5x + 3$

17) $y = 2x + 4$
18) $y = 4x + 12$
19) $y = 4x - 14$
20) $y = -2x$
21) $y = -3x + 2$
22) $y = 3x + 7$

Graphing Linear Inequalities

1) $y > 3x - 1$

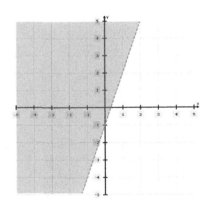

2) $y < -x + 4$

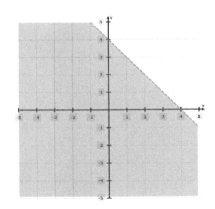

3) $y \leq -5x + 8$

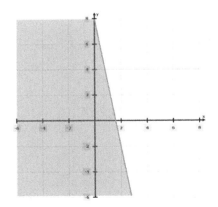

4) $2y \geq 8 + 6x$ 5) $y < 2x - 3$ 6) $4y \leq -6x + 2$

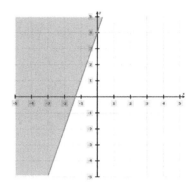

Finding Midpoint

1) $(-1, 0)$	10) $(4, 3)$	19) $(3, 11)$
2) $(1.5, 2.5)$	11) $(-1, 6)$	20) $(9, 4)$
3) $(2, 1)$	12) $(4, -2)$	21) $(2.5, -3.5)$
4) $(-2, 4)$	13) $(-3, 9)$	22) $(-1, -2)$
5) $(5, -4)$	14) $(11, 2)$	23) $(8, 1.5)$
6) $(-1, -5)$	15) $(4, 4)$	24) $(2, 1.5)$
7) $(0, 4)$	16) $(-5, 2)$	25) $(-3, 6)$
8) $(-4, 2)$	17) $(9, 9)$	26) $(13, -2)$
9) $(3, -1)$	18) $(2, -6)$	27) $(14, 22)$

Finding Distance of Two Points

1) 5	9) 20	17) 17
2) 5	10) 10	18) 26
3) 10	11) 26	19) 25
4) 13	12) 13	20) 13
5) 15	13) 15	21) 6 *square units*
6) 5	14) 17	22) 12 *units*
7) 17	15) 5	23) 14 *units*
8) 15	16) 13	

Chapter 9: Exponents and Variables

Math Topics that you'll learn in this Chapter:

- ✓ Multiplication Property of Exponents
- ✓ Division Property of Exponents
- ✓ Powers of Products and Quotients
- ✓ Zero and Negative Exponents
- ✓ Negative Exponents and Negative Bases
- ✓ Scientific Notation
- ✓ Radicals

69

Multiplication Property of Exponents

 Simplify and write the answer in exponential form.

1) $2 \times 2^2 =$

2) $5^3 \times 5 =$

3) $3^2 \times 3^2 =$

4) $4^2 \times 4^2 =$

5) $7^3 \times 7^2 \times 7 =$

6) $2 \times 2^2 \times 2^2 =$

7) $5^3 \times 5^2 \times 5 \times 5 =$

8) $2x \times x =$

9) $x^3 \times x^2 =$

10) $x^4 \times x^4 =$

11) $x^2 \times x^2 \times x^2 =$

12) $6x \times 6x =$

13) $2x^2 \times 2x^2 =$

14) $3x^2 \times x =$

15) $4x^4 \times 4x^4 \times 4x^4 =$

16) $2x^2 \times x^2 =$

17) $x^4 \times 3x =$

18) $x \times 2x^2 =$

19) $5x^4 \times 5x^4 =$

20) $2yx^2 \times 2x =$

21) $3x^4 \times y^2x^4 =$

22) $y^2x^3 \times y^5x^2 =$

23) $4yx^3 \times 2x^2y^3 =$

24) $6x^2 \times 6x^3y^4 =$

25) $3x^4y^5 \times 7x^2y^3 =$

26) $7x^2y^5 \times 9xy^3 =$

27) $7xy^4 \times 4x^3y^3 =$

28) $3x^5y^3 \times 8x^2y^3 =$

29) $3x \times y^5x^3 \times y^4 =$

30) $yx^2 \times 2y^2x^2 \times 2xy =$

31) $4yx^4 \times 5y^5x \times xy^3 =$

32) $7x^3 \times 10y^3x^5 \times 8yx^3 =$

Division Property of Exponents

Simplify.

1) $\dfrac{2^2}{2^3} =$

2) $\dfrac{2^4}{2^2} =$

3) $\dfrac{5^5}{5} =$

4) $\dfrac{3}{3^5} =$

5) $\dfrac{x}{x^3} =$

6) $\dfrac{3 \times 3^3}{3^2 \times 3^4} =$

7) $\dfrac{5^8}{5^3} =$

8) $\dfrac{5 \times 5^6}{5^2 \times 5^7} =$

9) $\dfrac{3^4 \times 3^7}{3^2 \times 3^8} =$

10) $\dfrac{5x}{10x^3} =$

11) $\dfrac{3x^3}{2x^5} =$

12) $\dfrac{12x^3}{14x^6} =$

13) $\dfrac{12x^3}{9y^8} =$

14) $\dfrac{25xy^4}{5x^6y^2} =$

15) $\dfrac{2x^4}{7x} =$

16) $\dfrac{16x^2y^8}{4x^3} =$

17) $\dfrac{12x^4}{15x^7y^9} =$

18) $\dfrac{12yx^4}{10yx^8} =$

19) $\dfrac{16x^4y}{9x^8y^2} =$

20) $\dfrac{5x^8}{20x^8} =$

21) $\dfrac{2x^{-5}}{9x^{-2}} =$

Powers of Products and Quotients

✎ **Simplify.**

1) $(4^2)^2 =$

2) $(6^2)^3 =$

3) $(2 \times 2^3)^4 =$

4) $(4 \times 4^4)^2 =$

5) $(3^3 \times 3^2)^3 =$

6) $(5^4 \times 5^5)^2 =$

7) $(2 \times 2^4)^2 =$

8) $(2^6)^2 =$

9) $(11x^5)^2 =$

10) $(4x^2y^4)^4 =$

11) $(2x^4y^4)^3 =$

12) $(3x^2y^2)^2 =$

13) $(3x^4y^3)^4 =$

14) $(2x^6y^8)^2 =$

15) $(12x^3x)^3 =$

16) $(2x^9x^6)^3 =$

17) $(5x^{10}y^3)^3 =$

18) $(4x^3x^3)^2 =$

19) $(3x^3 . 5x)^2 =$

20) $(10x^{11}y^3)^2 =$

21) $(9x^7y^5)^2 =$

22) $(4x^4y^6)^5 =$

23) $(3x . 4y^3)^2 =$

24) $\left(\dfrac{5x}{x^2}\right)^2 =$

25) $\left(\dfrac{x^4y^4}{x^2y^2}\right)^3 =$

26) $\left(\dfrac{25x}{5x^6}\right)^2 =$

27) $\left(\dfrac{x^8}{x^6y^2}\right)^2 =$

28) $\left(\dfrac{xy^2}{x^3y^3}\right)^{-2} =$

29) $\left(\dfrac{2xy^4}{x^3}\right)^2 =$

30) $\left(\dfrac{xy^4}{5xy^2}\right)^{-3} =$

Zero and Negative Exponents

✎ *Evaluate the following expressions.*

1) $1^{-1} =$

2) $2^{-2} =$

3) $0^{15} =$

4) $1^{-10} =$

5) $8^{-1} =$

6) $8^{-2} =$

7) $2^{-4} =$

8) $10^{-2} =$

9) $9^{-1} =$

10) $3^{-2} =$

11) $7^{-2} =$

12) $3^{-4} =$

13) $6^{-2} =$

14) $5^{-3} =$

15) $22^{-1} =$

16) $4^{-2} =$

17) $5^{-2} =$

18) $35^{-1} =$

19) $4^{-3} =$

20) $6^{-3} =$

21) $3^{-5} =$

22) $5^{-4} =$

23) $2^{-3} =$

24) $3^{-3} =$

25) $7^{-3} =$

26) $6^{-4} =$

27) $8^{-3} =$

28) $9^{-2} =$

29) $10^{-3} =$

30) $10^{-9} =$

31) $\left(\frac{1}{2}\right)^{-1}$

32) $\left(\frac{1}{2}\right)^{-2} =$

33) $\left(\frac{1}{3}\right)^{-2} =$

34) $\left(\frac{2}{3}\right)^{-2} =$

35) $\left(\frac{1}{5}\right)^{-3} =$

36) $\left(\frac{3}{4}\right)^{-2} =$

37) $\left(\frac{2}{5}\right)^{-2} =$

38) $\left(\frac{1}{2}\right)^{-8} =$

39) $\left(\frac{2}{5}\right)^{-3} =$

40) $\left(\frac{3}{7}\right)^{-2} =$

41) $\left(\frac{5}{6}\right)^{-3} =$

42) $\left(\frac{4}{9}\right)^{-2} =$

Negative Exponents and Negative Bases

✏️ **Simplify.**

1) $-6^{-1} =$

2) $-5^{-2} =$

3) $-2^{-4} =$

4) $-x^{-3} =$

5) $2x^{-1} =$

6) $-4x^{-3} =$

7) $-12x^{-5} =$

8) $-5x^{-2}y^{-3} =$

9) $20x^{-4}y^{-1} =$

10) $14a^{-6}b^{-7} =$

11) $-12x^2y^{-3} =$

12) $-\dfrac{25}{x^{-6}} =$

13) $-\dfrac{2x}{a^{-4}} =$

14) $\left(-\dfrac{1}{3}\right)^{-2} =$

15) $\left(-\dfrac{3}{4}\right)^{-2} =$

16) $-\dfrac{9}{a^{-7}b^{-2}} =$

17) $-\dfrac{5x}{x^{-3}} =$

18) $-\dfrac{a^{-3}}{b^{-2}} =$

19) $-\dfrac{5}{x^{-3}} =$

20) $\dfrac{7b}{-9c^{-4}} =$

21) $\dfrac{7ab}{a^{-3}b^{-1}} =$

22) $-\dfrac{5n^{-2}}{10p^{-3}} =$

23) $\dfrac{4ab^{-2}}{-3c^{-2}} =$

24) $\left(\dfrac{3a}{2c}\right)^{-2} =$

25) $\left(-\dfrac{5x}{3yz}\right)^{-3} =$

26) $\dfrac{4b^{-2}}{2c^3} =$

27) $\left(-\dfrac{x^3}{x^4}\right)^{-2} =$

28) $\left(-\dfrac{x^{-2}}{3x^2}\right)^{-3} =$

29) $\left(-\dfrac{x^{-4}}{x^2}\right)^{-2} =$

Scientific Notation

✍ *Write each number in scientific notation.*

1) 0.113 =

2) 0.02 =

3) 2.5 =

4) 20 =

5) 60 =

6) 0.004 =

7) 78 =

8) 1,600 =

9) 1,450 =

10) 91,000 =

11) 2,000,000 =

12) 0.0000006 =

13) 354,000 =

14) 0.000325 =

15) 0.00023 =

16) 56,000,000 =

17) 21,000 =

18) 78,000,000 =

19) 0.0000022 =

20) 0.00012 =

✍ *Write each number in standard notation.*

21) 3×10^{-1} =

22) 5×10^{-2} =

23) 1.2×10^{3} =

24) 2×10^{-4} =

25) 1.5×10^{-2} =

26) 4×10^{3} =

27) 9×10^{5} =

28) 1.12×10^{4} =

29) 3×10^{-5} =

30) 8.3×10^{-5} =

Radicals

✏️ *Simplify and write the answer.*

1) $\sqrt{0} =$ _____

2) $\sqrt{1} =$ _____

3) $\sqrt{4} =$ _____

4) $\sqrt{16} =$ _____

5) $\sqrt{9} =$ _____

6) $\sqrt{25} =$ _____

7) $\sqrt{49} =$ _____

8) $\sqrt{36} =$ _____

9) $\sqrt{64} =$ _____

10) $\sqrt{81} =$ _____

11) $\sqrt{121} =$ _____

12) $\sqrt{225} =$ _____

13) $\sqrt{144} =$ _____

14) $\sqrt{100} =$ _____

15) $\sqrt{256} =$ _____

16) $\sqrt{289} =$ _____

17) $\sqrt{324} =$ _____

18) $\sqrt{400} =$ _____

19) $\sqrt{900} =$ _____

20) $\sqrt{529} =$ _____

21) $\sqrt{90} =$ _____

22) $\sqrt{169} =$ _____

23) $\sqrt{196} =$ _____

24) $\sqrt{361} =$ _____

✏️ *Evaluate.*

25) $\sqrt{4} \times \sqrt{16} =$ _____

26) $\sqrt{25} \times \sqrt{64} =$ _____

27) $\sqrt{2} \times \sqrt{8} =$ _____

28) $\sqrt{6} \times \sqrt{6} =$ _____

29) $\sqrt{5} \times \sqrt{5} =$ _____

30) $\sqrt{8} \times \sqrt{8} =$ _____

31) $\sqrt{2} + \sqrt{2} =$ _____

32) $\sqrt{8} + \sqrt{8} =$ _____

33) $4\sqrt{5} - 2\sqrt{5} =$ _____

34) $3\sqrt{3} \times 2\sqrt{3} =$ _____

35) $8\sqrt{2} \times 2\sqrt{2} =$ _____

36) $6\sqrt{3} - \sqrt{12} =$ _____

Answers – Chapter 9

Multiplication Property of Exponents

1) 2^3
2) 5^4
3) 3^4
4) 4^4
5) 7^6
6) 2^5
7) 5^7
8) $2x^2$
9) x^5
10) x^8
11) x^6

12) $36x^2$
13) $4x^4$
14) $3x^3$
15) $64x^{12}$
16) $2x^4$
17) $3x^5$
18) $2x^3$
19) $25x^8$
20) $4x^3y$
21) $3x^8y^2$
22) x^5y^7

23) $8x^5y^4$
24) $36x^5y^4$
25) $21x^6y^8$
26) $63x^3y^8$
27) $28x^4y^7$
28) $24x^7y^6$
29) $3x^4y^9$
30) $4x^5y^4$
31) $20x^6y^9$
32) $560x^{11}y^4$

Division Property of Exponents

1) $\frac{1}{2}$
2) 2^2
3) 5^4
4) $\frac{1}{3^4}$
5) $\frac{1}{x^2}$
6) $\frac{1}{3^2}$
7) 5^5
8) $\frac{1}{25}$

9) 3
10) $\frac{1}{2x^2}$
11) $\frac{3}{2x^2}$
12) $\frac{6}{7x^3}$
13) $\frac{4x^3}{3y^8}$
14) $\frac{5y^2}{x^5}$
15) $\frac{2x^3}{7}$

16) $\frac{4y^8}{x}$
17) $\frac{4}{5x^3y^9}$
18) $\frac{6}{5x^4}$
19) $\frac{16}{9x^4y}$
20) $\frac{1}{4}$
21) $\frac{2}{9x^3}$

Powers of Products and Quotients

1) 4^4
2) 6^6
3) 2^{16}
4) 4^{10}
5) 3^{15}
6) 5^{18}
7) 2^{10}
8) 2^{12}

9) $121x^{10}$
10) $256x^8y^{16}$
11) $8x^{12}y^{12}$
12) $9x^4y^4$
13) $81x^{16}y^{12}$
14) $4x^{12}y^{16}$
15) $1,728x^{12}$
16) $8x^{45}$

17) $125x^{30}y^9$
18) $16x^{12}$
19) $225x^8$
20) $100x^{22}y^6$
21) $81x^{14}y^{10}$
22) $1,024x^{20}y^{30}$

Effortless
Math
Education

23) $144x^2y^6$

24) $\frac{25}{x^2}$

25) x^6y^6

26) $\frac{25}{x^{10}}$

27) $\frac{x^4}{y^4}$

28) x^4y^2

29) $\frac{4y^8}{x^4}$

30) $\frac{125}{y^6}$

Zero and Negative Exponents

1) 1

2) $\frac{1}{4}$

3) 0

4) 1

5) $\frac{1}{8}$

6) $\frac{1}{64}$

7) $\frac{1}{16}$

8) $\frac{1}{100}$

9) $\frac{1}{9}$

10) $\frac{1}{9}$

11) $\frac{1}{49}$

12) $\frac{1}{81}$

13) $\frac{1}{36}$

14) $\frac{1}{125}$

15) $\frac{1}{22}$

16) $\frac{1}{16}$

17) $\frac{1}{25}$

18) $\frac{1}{35}$

19) $\frac{1}{64}$

20) $\frac{1}{216}$

21) $\frac{1}{243}$

22) $\frac{1}{625}$

23) $\frac{1}{8}$

24) $\frac{1}{27}$

25) $\frac{1}{343}$

26) $\frac{1}{1,296}$

27) $\frac{1}{512}$

28) $\frac{1}{81}$

29) $\frac{1}{1,000}$

30) $\frac{1}{1,000,000,000}$

31) 2

32) 4

33) 9

34) $\frac{9}{4}$

35) 125

36) $\frac{16}{9}$

37) $\frac{25}{4}$

38) 256

39) $\frac{125}{8}$

40) $\frac{49}{9}$

41) $\frac{216}{125}$

42) $\frac{81}{16}$

Negative Exponents and Negative Bases

1) $-\frac{1}{6}$

2) $-\frac{1}{25}$

3) $-\frac{1}{16}$

4) $-\frac{1}{x^3}$

5) $\frac{2}{x}$

6) $-\frac{4}{x^3}$

7) $-\frac{12}{x^5}$

8) $-\frac{5}{x^2y^3}$

9) $\frac{20}{x^4y}$

10) $\frac{14}{a^6b^7}$

11) $-\frac{12x^2}{y^3}$

12) $-25x^6$

13) $-2xa^4$

14) 9

15) $\frac{16}{9}$

16) $-9a^7b^2$

17) $-5x^4$

18) $-\frac{b^2}{a^3}$

19) $-5x^3$

20) $-\frac{7bc^4}{9}$

21) $7a^4b^2$

22) $-\frac{p^3}{2n^2}$

23) $-\frac{4ac^2}{3b^2}$

24) $\frac{4c^2}{9a^2}$

25) $-\frac{27y^3z^3}{125x^3}$

26) $\frac{2}{b^2c^3}$

27) x^2

28) $-27x^{12}$

29) x^{12}

Scientific Notation

1) 1.13×10^{-1}

2) 2×10^{-2}

3) 2.5×10^0

4) 2×10^1

5) 6×10^1

6) 4×10^{-3}

7) 7.8×10^1

8) 1.6×10^3

9) 1.45×10^3

10) 9.1×10^4

11) 2×10^6

12) 6×10^{-7}

13) 3.54×10^5

14) 3.25×10^{-4}

15) 2.3×10^{-4}

16) 5.6×10^7

17) 2.1×10^4

18) 7.8×10^7

19) 2.2×10^{-6}

20) 1.2×10^{-4}

21) 0.3

22) 0.05

23) $1,200$

24) 0.0002

25) 0.015

26) $4,000$

27) $900,000$

28) $11,200$

29) 0.00003

30) 0.000083

Radicals

1) 0

2) 1

3) 2

4) 4

5) 3

6) 5

7) 7

8) 6

9) 8

10) 9

11) 11

12) 15

13) 12

14) 10

15) 16

16) 17

17) 18

18) 20

19) 30

20) 23

21) $3\sqrt{10}$

22) 13

23) 14

24) 19

25) 8

26) 40

27) 4

28) 6

29) 5

30) 8

31) $2\sqrt{2}$

32) $2\sqrt{8}$

33) $2\sqrt{5}$

34) 18

35) 32

36) $4\sqrt{3}$

Effortless Math Education

Chapter 10:
Polynomials

Math Topics that you'll learn in this Chapter:

- ✓ Simplifying Polynomials
- ✓ Adding and Subtracting Polynomials
- ✓ Multiplying Monomials
- ✓ Multiplying and Dividing Monomials
- ✓ Multiplying a Polynomial and a Monomial
- ✓ Multiplying Binomials
- ✓ Factoring Trinomials

81

Simplifying Polynomials

✎ *Simplify each expression.*

1) $5(2x - 10) =$

2) $2x(4x - 2) =$

3) $4x(5x - 3) =$

4) $3x(7x + 3) =$

5) $4x(8x - 4) =$

6) $5x(5x + 4) =$

7) $(2x - 3)(x - 4) =$

8) $(x - 5)(3x + 4) =$

9) $(x - 5)(x - 3) =$

10) $(3x + 8)(3x - 8) =$

11) $(3x - 8)(3x - 4) =$

12) $3x^2 + 3x^2 - 2x^3 =$

13) $2x - x^2 + 6x^3 + 4 =$

14) $5x + 2x^2 - 9x^3 =$

15) $7x^2 + 5x^4 - 2x^3 =$

16) $-3x^2 + 5x^3 + 6x^4 =$

17) $-8x^2 + 2x^3 - 10x^4 + 5x =$

18) $11 - 6x^2 + 5x^2 - 12x^3 + 22 =$

19) $2x^2 - 2x + 3x^3 + 12x - 22x =$

20) $11 - 4x^2 + 3x^2 - 7x^3 + 3 =$

21) $2x^5 - x^3 + 8x^2 - 2x^5 =$

22) $(2x^3 - 1) + (3x^3 - 2x^3) =$

23) $3(4x^4 - 4x^3 - 5x^4) =$

24) $-5(x^6 + 10) - 8(14 - x^6) =$

25) $3x^2 - 5x^3 - x + 10 - 2x^2 =$

26) $11 - 3x^2 + 2x^2 - 5x^3 + 7 =$

27) $(8x^2 - 3x) - (5x - 5 - 8x^2) =$

28) $3x^2 - 5x^3 - x(2x^2 + 4x) =$

29) $4x + 8x^3 - 4 - 3(x^3 - 2) =$

30) $12 + 2x^2 - (8x^3 - x^2 + 6x^3) =$

31) $-2(x^4 + 6) - 5(10 + x^4) =$

32) $(8x^3 - 2x) - (5x - 2x^3) =$

Adding and Subtracting Polynomials

✎ *Add or subtract expressions.*

1) $(-x^2 - 2) + (2x^2 + 1) =$

2) $(2x^2 + 3) - (3 - 4x^2) =$

3) $(2x^3 + 3x^2) - (x^3 + 8) =$

4) $(4x^3 - x^2) + (3x^2 - 5x) =$

5) $(7x^3 + 9x) - (3x^3 + 2) =$

6) $(2x^3 - 2) + (2x^3 + 2) =$

7) $(4x^3 + 5) - (7 - 2x^3) =$

8) $(4x^2 + 2x^3) - (2x^3 + 5) =$

9) $(4x^2 - x) + (3x - 5x^2) =$

10) $(7x + 9) - (3x + 9) =$

11) $(4x^4 - 2x) - (6x - 2x^4) =$

12) $(12x - 4x^3) - (8x^3 + 6x) =$

13) $(2x^3 - 8x^2) - (5x^2 - 3x) =$

14) $(2x^2 - 6) + (9x^2 - 4x^3) =$

15) $(4x^3 + 3x^4) - (x^4 - 5x^3) =$

16) $(-2x^3 - 2x) + (6x - 2x^3) =$

17) $(2x - 4x^4) - (8x^4 + 3x) =$

18) $(2x - 8x^2) - (5x^4 - 3x^2) =$

19) $(2x^3 - 6) + (9x^3 - 4x^2) =$

20) $(4x^3 + 3x^4) - (x^4 - 5x^3) =$

21) $(-2x^2 + 10x^4 + x^3) + (4x^3 + 3x^4 + 8x^2) =$

22) $(3x^2 - 6x^5 - 2x) - (-2x^2 - 6x^5 + 2x) =$

23) $(5x + 9x^3 - 3x^5) + (8x^3 + 3x^5 - 2x) =$

24) $(3x^5 - 2x^4 - 4x) - (4x^2 + 10x^4 - 3x) =$

25) $(13x^2 - 6x^5 - 2x) - (-10x^2 - 11x^5 + 9x) =$

26) $(-12x^4 + 10x^5 + 2x^3) + (14x^3 + 23x^5 + 8x^4) =$

Multiplying Monomials

✎ *Simplify each expression.*

1) $4u^9 \times (-2u^3) =$

2) $(-2p^7) \times (-3p^2) =$

3) $3xy^2z^3 \times 2z^2 =$

4) $5u^5t \times 3ut^2 =$

5) $(-9a^6) \times (-5a^2b^4) =$

6) $-2a^3b^2 \times 4a^2b =$

7) $2xy^2 \times x^2y^3 =$

8) $3p^2q^4 \times (-2pq^3) =$

9) $4s^5t^2 \times 4st^3 =$

10) $(-6x^3y^2) \times 3x^2y =$

11) $2xy^2z \times 4z^2 =$

12) $4xy \times x^2y =$

13) $4pq^3 \times (-2p^4q) =$

14) $8s^4t^2 \times st^5 =$

15) $12p^3 \times (-3p^4) =$

16) $(-4p^2q^3r) \times 6pq^2r^3 =$

17) $(-8a^4) \times -12a^6b =$

18) $3u^4v^2 \times (-7u^2v^3) =$

19) $4u^3 \times (-2u) =$

20) $-6xy^2 \times 3x^2y =$

21) $12y^2z^3 \times (-y^2z) =$

22) $5a^2bc^2 \times 2abc^2 =$

23) $(-7p^3q^5) \times (-4p^2q^3) =$

24) $4u^5v^2 \times (-8u^3v^2) =$

25) $12y^3z^4 \times (-y^6z) =$

26) $(-4pq^5r^3) \times 6p^2q^4r =$

27) $5ab^4c^2 \times 2a^5bc^2 =$

28) $2x^4yz^3 \times 3x^2y^4z^2 =$

Multiplying and Dividing Monomials

✑ *Simplify each expression.*

1) $(2x^2)(x^3) =$

2) $(3x^4)(2x^4) =$

3) $(6x^5)(2x^2) =$

4) $(4x^3)(3x^5) =$

5) $(15x^4)(3x^9) =$

6) $(2yx^2)(3y^2x^3) =$

7) $(2x^2y)(x^2y^3) =$

8) $(-2x^3y^4)(3x^3y^2) =$

9) $(-5x^3y^2)(-2x^4y^5) =$

10) $(9x^5y)(-3x^3y^3) =$

11) $(8x^7y^2)(6x^5y^4) =$

12) $(7x^4y^6)(4x^3y^4) =$

13) $(12x^2y^9)(7x^9y^{12}) =$

14) $(6x^2y^5)(5x^3y^2) =$

15) $(9x^2y^9)(4x^{10}y^9) =$

16) $(-10x^4y^8)(2x^9y^5) =$

17) $\dfrac{4x^2y^3}{xy^2} =$

18) $\dfrac{2x^4y^3}{2x^3y} =$

19) $\dfrac{8x^2y^2}{4xy} =$

20) $\dfrac{6x^3y^4}{2x^2y^3} =$

21) $\dfrac{12x^6y^8}{4x^4y^2} =$

22) $\dfrac{26x^9y^5}{2x^3y^4} =$

23) $\dfrac{80x^{12}y^9}{10x^6y^7} =$

24) $\dfrac{95x^{18}y^7}{5x^9y^2} =$

25) $\dfrac{200x^3y^8}{40x^3y^7} =$

26) $\dfrac{-15x^{17}y^{13}}{3x^6y^9} =$

27) $\dfrac{-64x^8y^{10}}{8x^3y^7} =$

Find more at bit.ly/2WHp4

Multiplying a Polynomial and a Monomial

✍ *Find each product.*

1) $x(x + 3) =$

2) $8(2 - x) =$

3) $2x(2x + 1) =$

4) $x(-x + 3) =$

5) $3x(3x - 2) =$

6) $5(3x - 6y) =$

7) $8x(7x - 4) =$

8) $3x(9x + 2y) =$

9) $6x(x + 2y) =$

10) $9x(2x + 4y) =$

11) $12x(3x + 9) =$

12) $11x(2x - 11y) =$

13) $2x(6x - 6y) =$

14) $2x(3x - 6y + 3) =$

15) $5x(3x^2 + 2y^2) =$

16) $13x(4x + 8y) =$

17) $5(2x^2 - 9y^2) =$

18) $3x(-2x^2y + 3y) =$

19) $-2(2x^2 - 2xy + 2) =$

20) $3(x^2 - 4xy - 8) =$

21) $2x(2x^2 - 3xy + 2x) =$

22) $-x(-x^2 - 5x + 4xy) =$

23) $9(x^2 + xy - 8y^2) =$

24) $3x(2x^2 - 3x + 8) =$

25) $20(2x^2 - 8x - 5) =$

26) $x^2(-x^2 + 3x + 7) =$

27) $x^3(x^2 + 12 - 2x) =$

28) $6x^3(3x^2 - 2x + 2) =$

29) $8x^2(3x^2 - 5xy + 7y^2) =$

30) $2x^2(3x^2 - 5x + 12) =$

31) $2x^3(2x^2 + 5x - 4) =$

32) $5x(6x^2 - 5xy + 2y^2) =$

Multiplying Binomials

✎ *Find each product.*

1) $(x + 2)(x + 2) =$

2) $(x - 3)(x + 2) =$

3) $(x - 2)(x - 4) =$

4) $(x + 3)(x + 2) =$

5) $(x - 4)(x - 5) =$

6) $(x + 5)(x + 2) =$

7) $(x - 6)(x + 3) =$

8) $(x - 8)(x - 4) =$

9) $(x + 2)(x + 8) =$

10) $(x - 2)(x + 4) =$

11) $(x + 4)(x + 4) =$

12) $(x + 5)(x + 5) =$

13) $(x - 3)(x + 3) =$

14) $(x - 2)(x + 2) =$

15) $(x + 3)(x + 3) =$

16) $(x + 4)(x + 6) =$

17) $(x - 7)(x + 7) =$

18) $(x - 7)(x + 2) =$

19) $(2x + 2)(x + 3) =$

20) $(2x - 3)(2x + 4) =$

21) $(x - 8)(2x + 8) =$

22) $(x - 7)(x - 6) =$

23) $(x - 8)(x + 8) =$

24) $(3x - 2)(4x + 2) =$

25) $(2x - 5)(x + 7) =$

26) $(5x - 4)(3x + 3) =$

27) $(6x + 9)(4x + 9) =$

28) $(2x - 6)(5x + 6) =$

29) $(x + 4)(4x - 8) =$

30) $(6x - 4)(6x + 4) =$

31) $(3x + 3)(3x - 4) =$

32) $(x^2 + 2)(x^2 - 2) =$

Factoring Trinomials

✎ **Factor each trinomial.**

1) $x^2 + 8x + 15 =$

2) $x^2 - 5x + 6 =$

3) $x^2 + 6x + 8 =$

4) $x^2 - 6x + 8 =$

5) $x^2 - 8x + 16 =$

6) $x^2 - 7x + 12 =$

7) $x^2 + 11x + 18 =$

8) $x^2 + 2x - 24 =$

9) $x^2 + 4x - 12 =$

10) $x^2 - 10x + 9 =$

11) $x^2 + 5x - 14 =$

12) $x^2 - 6x - 27 =$

13) $x^2 - 11x - 42 =$

14) $x^2 + 22x + 121 =$

15) $6x^2 + x - 12 =$

16) $x^2 - 17x + 30 =$

17) $3x^2 + 11x - 4 =$

18) $10x^2 + 33x - 7 =$

19) $x^2 + 24x + 144 =$

20) $8x^2 + 10x - 3 =$

✎ **Solve each problem.**

21) The area of a rectangle is $x^2 + 2x - 24$. If the width of rectangle is $x - 4$, what is its length? _____

22) The area of a parallelogram is $8x^2 + 2x - 6$ and its height is $2x + 2$. What is the base of the parallelogram? _____

23) The area of a rectangle is $18x^2 + 9x - 2$. If the width of the rectangle is $6x - 1$, what is its length? _____

Answers – Chapter 10

Simplifying Polynomials

1) $10x - 50$
2) $8x^2 - 4x$
3) $20x^2 - 12x$
4) $21x^2 + 9x$
5) $32x^2 - 16x$
6) $25x^2 + 20x$
7) $2x^2 - 11x + 12$
8) $3x^2 - 11x - 20$
9) $x^2 - 8x + 15$
10) $9x^2 - 64$
11) $9x^2 - 36x + 32$
12) $-2x^3 + 6x^2$
13) $6x^3 - x^2 + 2x + 4$
14) $-9x^3 + 2x^2 + 5x$
15) $5x^4 - 2x^3 + 7x^2$
16) $6x^4 + 5x^3 - 3x^2$

17) $-10x^4 + 2x^3 - 8x^2 + 5x$
18) $-12x^3 - x^2 + 33$
19) $3x^3 + 2x^2 - 12x$
20) $-7x^3 - x^2 + 14$
21) $-x^3 + 8x^2$
22) $3x^3 - 1$
23) $-3x^4 - 12x^3$
24) $3x^6 - 162$
25) $-5x^3 + x^2 - x + 10$
26) $-5x^3 - x^2 + 18$
27) $16x^2 - 8x + 5$
28) $-7x^3 - x^2$
29) $5x^3 + 4x + 2$
30) $-14x^3 + 3x^2 + 12$
31) $-7x^4 - 62$
32) $10x^3 - 7x$

Adding and Subtracting Polynomials

1) $x^2 - 1$
2) $6x^2$
3) $x^3 + 3x^2 - 8$
4) $4x^3 + 2x^2 - 5x$
5) $4x^3 + 9x - 2$
6) $4x^3$
7) $6x^3 - 2$
8) $4x^2 - 5$
9) $-x^2 + 2x$
10) $4x$
11) $6x^4 - 8x$
12) $-12x^3 + 6x$
13) $2x^3 - 13x^2 + 3x$

14) $-4x^3 + 11x^2 - 6$
15) $2x^4 + 9x^3$
16) $-4x^3 + 4x$
17) $-12x^4 - x$
18) $-5x^4 - 5x^2 + 2x$
19) $11x^3 - 4x^2 - 6$
20) $2x^4 + 9x^3$
21) $13x^4 + 5x^3 + 6x^2$
22) $5x^2 - 4x$
23) $17x^3 + 3x$
24) $3x^5 - 12x^4 - 4x^2 - x$
25) $5x^5 + 23x^2 - 11x$
26) $33x^5 - 4x^4 + 16x^3$

Multiplying Monomials

1) $-8u^{12}$
2) $6p^9$
3) $6xy^2z^5$
4) $15u^6t^3$

Effortless Math Education

5) $45a^8b^4$

6) $-8a^5b^3$

7) $2x^3y^5$

8) $-6p^3q^7$

9) $16s^6t^5$

10) $-18x^5y^3$

11) $8xy^2z^3$

12) $4x^3y^2$

13) $-8p^5q^4$

14) $8s^5t^7$

15) $-36p^7$

16) $-24p^3q^5r^4$

17) $96a^{10}b$

18) $-21u^6v^5$

19) $-8u^4$

20) $-18x^3y^3$

21) $-12y^4z^4$

22) $10a^3b^2c^4$

23) $28p^5q^8$

24) $-32u^8v^4$

25) $-12y^9z^5$

26) $-24p^3q^9r^4$

27) $10a^6b^5c^4$

28) $6x^6y^5z^5$

Multiplying and Dividing Monomials

1) $2x^5$

2) $6x^8$

3) $12x^7$

4) $12x^8$

5) $45x^{13}$

6) $6x^5y^3$

7) $2x^4y^4$

8) $-6x^6y^6$

9) $10x^7y^7$

10) $-27x^8y^4$

11) $48x^{12}y^6$

12) $28x^7y^{10}$

13) $84x^{11}y^{21}$

14) $30x^5y^7$

15) $36x^{12}y^{18}$

16) $-20x^{13}y^{13}$

17) $4xy$

18) xy^2

19) $2xy$

20) $3xy$

21) $3x^2y^6$

22) $13x^6y$

23) $8x^6y^2$

24) $19x^9y^5$

25) $5y$

26) $-5x^{11}y^4$

27) $-8x^5y^3$

Multiplying a Polynomial and a Monomial

1) $x^2 + 3x$

2) $-8x + 16$

3) $4x^2 + 2x$

4) $-x^2 + 3x$

5) $9x^2 - 6x$

6) $15x - 30y$

7) $56x^2 - 32x$

8) $27x^2 + 6xy$

9) $6x^2 + 12xy$

10) $18x^2 + 36xy$

11) $36x^2 + 108x$

12) $22x^2 - 121xy$

13) $12x^2 - 12xy$

14) $6x^2 - 12xy + 6x$

15) $15x^3 + 10xy^2$

16) $52x^2 + 104xy$

17) $10x^2 - 45y^2$

18) $-6x^3y + 9xy$

19) $-4x^2 + 4xy - 4$

20) $3x^2 - 12xy - 24$

21) $4x^3 - 6x^2y + 4x^2$

22) $x^3 + 5x^2 - 4x^2y$

23) $9x^2 + 9xy - 72y^2$

24) $6x^3 - 9x^2 + 24x$

25) $40x^2 - 160x - 100$

26) $-x^4 + 3x^3 + 7x^2$

27) $x^5 - 2x^4 + 12x^3$

28) $18x^5 - 12x^4 + 12x^3$

29) $24x^4 - 40x^3y + 56x^2y^2$

30) $6x^4 - 10x^3 + 24x^2$

31) $4x^5 + 10x^4 - 8x^3$

32) $30x^3 - 25x^2y + 10xy^2$

Multiplying Binomials

1) $x^2 + 4x + 4$
2) $x^2 - x - 6$
3) $x^2 - 6x + 8$
4) $x^2 + 5x + 6$
5) $x^2 - 9x + 20$
6) $x^2 + 7x + 10$
7) $x^2 - 3x - 18$
8) $x^2 - 12x + 32$
9) $x^2 + 10x + 16$
10) $x^2 + 2x - 8$
11) $x^2 + 8x + 16$
12) $x^2 + 10x + 25$
13) $x^2 - 9$
14) $x^2 - 4$
15) $x^2 + 6x + 9$
16) $x^2 + 10x + 24$

17) $x^2 - 49$
18) $x^2 - 5x - 14$
19) $2x^2 + 8x + 6$
20) $4x^2 + 2x - 12$
21) $2x^2 - 8x - 64$
22) $x^2 - 13x + 42$
23) $x^2 - 64$
24) $12x^2 - 2x - 4$
25) $2x^2 + 9x - 35$
26) $15x^2 + 3x - 12$
27) $24x^2 + 90x + 81$
28) $10x^2 - 18x - 36$
29) $4x^2 + 8x - 32$
30) $36x^2 - 16$
31) $9x^2 - 3x - 12$
32) $x^4 - 4$

Factoring Trinomials

1) $(x + 3)(x + 5)$
2) $(x - 2)(x - 3)$
3) $(x + 4)(x + 2)$
4) $(x - 2)(x - 4)$
5) $(x - 4)(x - 4)$
6) $(x - 3)(x - 4)$
7) $(x + 2)(x + 9)$
8) $(x + 6)(x - 4)$

9) $(x - 2)(x + 6)$
10) $(x - 1)(x - 9)$
11) $(x - 2)(x + 7)$
12) $(x - 9)(x + 3)$
13) $(x + 3)(x - 14)$
14) $(x + 11)(x + 11)$
15) $(2x + 3)(3x - 4)$
16) $(x - 15)(x - 2)$

17) $(3x - 1)(x + 4)$
18) $(5x - 1)(2x + 7)$
19) $(x + 12)(x + 12)$
20) $(4x - 1)(2x + 3)$
21) $(x + 6)$
22) $(4x - 3)$
23) $(3x + 2)$

Effortless
Math
Education

Chapter 11: Geometry and Solid Figures

Math Topics that you'll learn in this Chapter:

- ✓ The Pythagorean Theorem
- ✓ Complementary and Supplementary Angles
- ✓ Parallel Lines and Transversals
- ✓ Triangles
- ✓ Special Right Triangles
- ✓ Polygons
- ✓ Trapezoids
- ✓ Cubes
- ✓ Rectangle Prisms
- ✓ Cylinder

Pythagorean Theorem

✏️ *Do the following lengths form a right triangle?*

1)

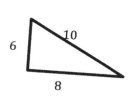

2)

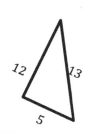

3)

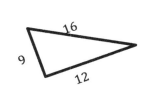

4)

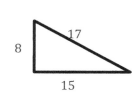

5)

6)

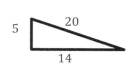

7)

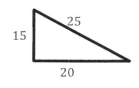

8)

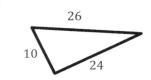

✏️ *Find the missing side.*

9)

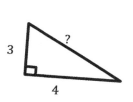

10)

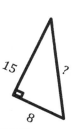

11)

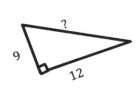

12)

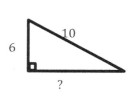

13)

14)

15)

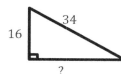

16)

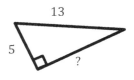

Complementary and Supplementary Angles

 Find the missing measurement in the pair of angles.

1) $x =$ ___

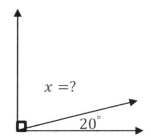

$x =?$

$20°$

2) $x =$ ___

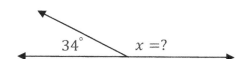

$34°$ $x =?$

3) *The measure of an angle is* **58°**. *What is the measure of its complementary*

   angle? _____

4) *The measure of an angle is* 135°. *What is the measure of its supplementary*

   angle? _____

5) *Angles A and B are complementary. If* $A = 3x - 8$ *and* $B = 5x + 10$, *what*

   is the measure of each angle?

   $A =$ _____ $B =$ _____

Parallel Lines and Transversals

✎ *Find the measure of each angle indicated.*

1) ? = ____

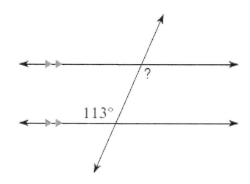

?

111°

2) ? = ____

?

113°

✎ *In the following diagrams, solve for x.*

3) $x =$ ____

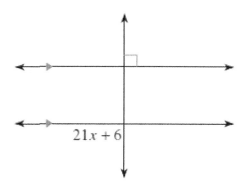

$21x + 6$

4) $x =$ ____

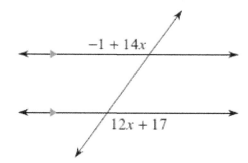

$-1 + 14x$

$12x + 17$

Triangles

✎ **Find the measure of the unknown angle in each triangle.**

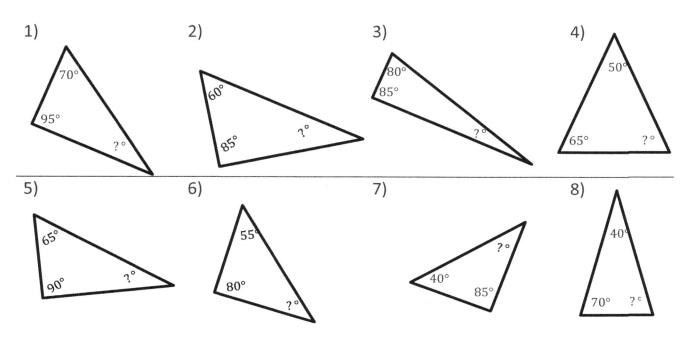

1) 70° 95° ?°

2) 60° 85° ?°

3) 80° 85° ?°

4) 50° 65° ?°

5) 65° 90° ?°

6) 55° 80° ?°

7) ?° 40° 85°

8) 40° 70° ?°

✎ **Find area of each triangle.**

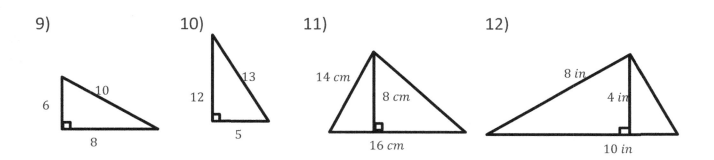

9) 10 6 8

10) 13 12 5

11) 14 cm 8 cm 16 cm

12) 8 in 4 in 10 in

Special Right Triangles

✎ *Find the value of x and y in each triangle.*

1) $x =$ ___ $y =$ ___

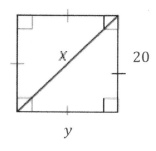

2) $x =$ ___ $y =$ ___

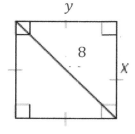

3) $x =$ ___ $y =$ ___

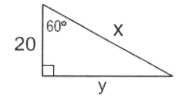

4) $x =$ ___ $y =$ ___

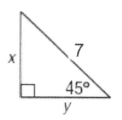

5) $x =$ ___ $y =$ ___

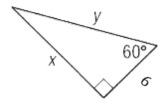

6) $x =$ ___ $y =$ ___

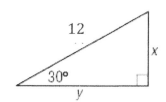

Polygons

 Find the perimeter of each shape.

1)

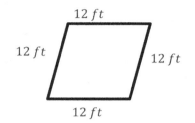

12 ft
12 ft   12 ft
12 ft

2)

10 in
8 in   8 in
10 in

3)

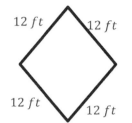

12 ft   12 ft
12 ft   12 ft

4) Square

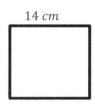

14 cm

5) Regular hexagon

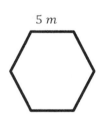

5 m

6)

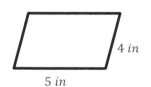

4.5 cm
5.5 cm
4 cm
5.5 cm
4.5 cm

7) Parallelogram

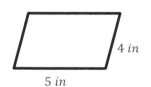

5 in   4 in

8) Square

6 m

 Find the area of each shape.

9) Parallelogram

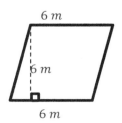

6 m
6 m
6 m

10) Rectangle

10 in
8 in

11) Rectangle

7 km
5 km

12) Square

7 in

Trapezoids

✍ *Find the area of each trapezoid.*

1)

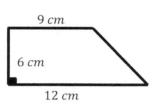

9 cm

6 cm

12 cm

2)

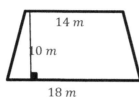

14 m

10 m

18 m

3)

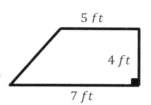

5 ft

4 ft

7 ft

4)

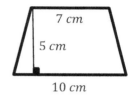

7 cm

5 cm

10 cm

5)

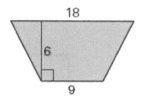

18

6

9

6)

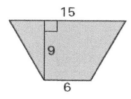

15

9

6

7)

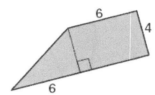

6

4

6

8)

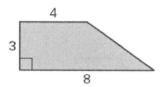

4

3

8

✍ **Solve.**

9) A trapezoid has an area of $60\ cm^2$ and its height is $6\ cm$ and one base is $8\ cm$. What is the other base length? _____

10) If a trapezoid has an area of $65\ ft^2$ and the lengths of the bases are $12\ ft$ and $14\ ft$, find the height. _____

11) If a trapezoid has an area of $180\ m^2$ and its height is $12\ m$ and one base is $20\ m$, find the other base length. _____

12) The area of a trapezoid is $625\ ft^2$ and its height is $25\ ft$. If one base of the trapezoid is $15\ ft$, what is the other base length? _____

Cubes

✏️ **Find the volume of each cube.**

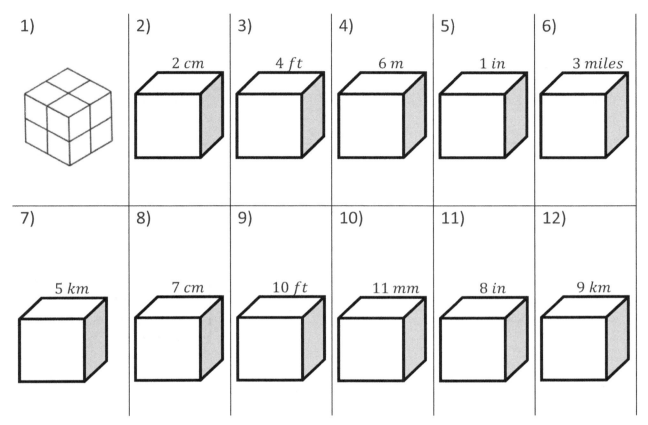

1)

2)
2 cm

3)
4 ft

4)
6 m

5)
1 in

6)
3 miles

7)
5 km

8)
7 cm

9)
10 ft

10)
11 mm

11)
8 in

12)
9 km

✏️ **Find the surface area of each cube.**

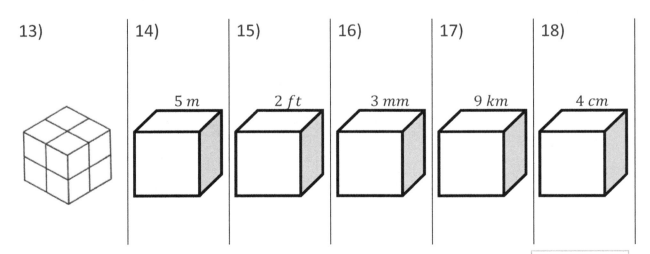

13)

14)
5 m

15)
2 ft

16)
3 mm

17)
9 km

18)
4 cm

Rectangular Prism

✎ **Find the volume of each Rectangular Prism.**

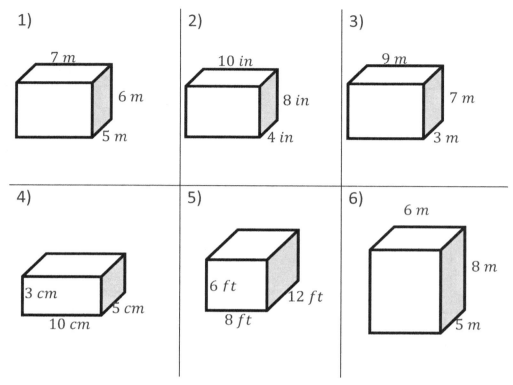

1)
7 m
6 m
5 m

2)
10 in
8 in
4 in

3)
9 m
7 m
3 m

4)
3 cm
5 cm
10 cm

5)
6 ft
12 ft
8 ft

6)
6 m
8 m
5 m

✎ **Find the surface area of each Rectangular Prism.**

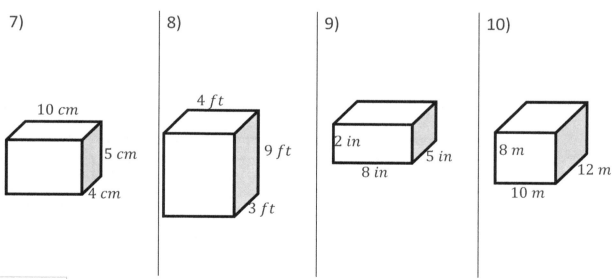

7)
10 cm
5 cm
4 cm

8)
4 ft
9 ft
3 ft

9)
2 in
5 in
8 in

10)
8 m
12 m
10 m

Cylinder

✎ *Find the volume of each Cylinder. Round your answer to the nearest tenth.* (π = 3.14)

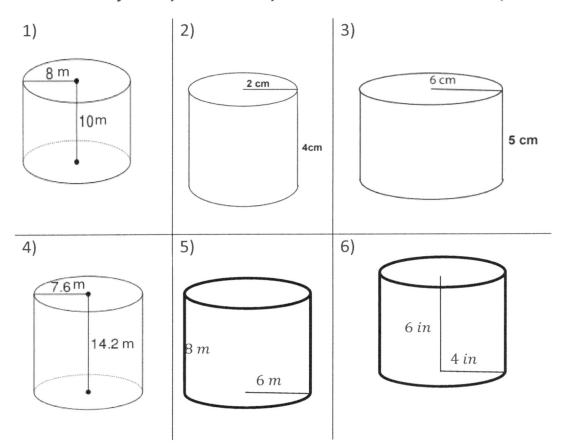

1) 8 m 10m

2) 2 cm 4cm

3) 6 cm 5 cm

4) 7.6 m 14.2 m

5) 8 m 6 m

6) 6 in 4 in

✎ *Find the surface area of each Cylinder.* (π = 3.14)

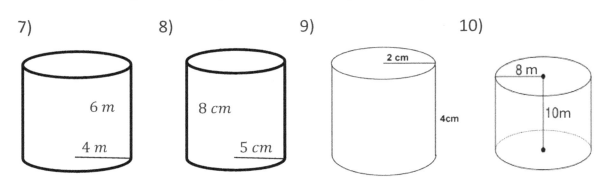

7) 6 m 4 m

8) 8 cm 5 cm

9) 2 cm 4cm

10) 8 m 10m

Answers – Chapter 11

Pythagorean Theorem

1) Yes

2) Yes

3) No

4) Yes

5) No

6) No

7) Yes

8) Yes

9) 5

10) 17

11) 15

12) 8

13) 5

14) 30

15) 30

16) 12

Complementary and Supplementary Angles

1) $70°$

2) $146°$

3) $32°$

4) $45°$

5) $A = 25°, B = 65°$

Parallel lines and Transversals

1) $111°$

2) $113°$

3) 4

4) 9

Triangles

1) 15°

2) 35°

3) 15°

4) 65°

5) 25°

6) 45°

7) 55°

8) 70°

9) 24 *square unites*

10) 30 *square unites*

11) 64 *square centimeters*

12) 20 *square inches*

Special Right Triangles

1) $x = 20\sqrt{2} \ \ y = 20$

2) $x = 4\sqrt{2} \ \ y = 4\sqrt{2}$

3) $x = 40 \ \ y = 20\sqrt{3}$

4) $x = \frac{7\sqrt{2}}{2} \ \ y = \frac{7\sqrt{2}}{2}$

5) $x = 6\sqrt{3} \ \ y = 12$

6) $x = 6 \ \ y = 6\sqrt{3}$

Polygons

1) $48 \ ft$

2) $36 \ in$

3) $48 \ ft$

4) $56 \ cm$

5) $30 \ m$

6) $20 \ cm$

7) $18 \ in$

8) $24 \ m$

9) $36 \ m^2$

10) $80 \ in^2$

11) $35 \ km^2$

12) $49 \ in^2$

Effortless

Math

Education

Trapezoids

1) $63\ cm^2$
2) $160\ m^2$
3) $24\ ft^2$
4) $42.5\ cm^2$

5) 81
6) 94.5
7) 36
8) 18
9) $12\ cm$

10) $5\ ft$
11) $10\ m$
12) $35\ ft$

Cubes

1) $8\ square\ units$
2) $8\ cm^3$
3) $64\ ft^3$
4) $216\ m^3$
5) $1\ in^3$
6) $27\ miles^3$

7) $125\ km^3$
8) $343\ cm^3$
9) $1,000\ ft^3$
10) $1,331\ mm^3$
11) $512\ in^3$
12) $729\ km^3$

13) $24\ square\ units$
14) $150\ m^2$
15) $24\ ft^2$
16) $54\ mm^2$
17) $486\ km^2$
18) $96\ cm^2$

Rectangular Prism

1) $210\ m^3$
2) $320\ in^3$
3) $189\ m^3$
4) $150\ cm^3$

5) $576\ ft^3$
6) $240\ m^3$
7) $220\ cm^2$
8) $150\ ft^2$

9) $132\ in2$
10) $592\ m^2$

Cylinder

1) $2,009.6\ m^3$
2) $50.24\ cm^3$
3) $565.2\ cm^3$
4) $2,575.4\ m^3$

5) $904.3\ m^3$
6) $301.4\ in^3$
7) $251.2\ m^2$
8) $408.2\ cm^2$

9) $75.4\ cm^2$
10) $904.3\ m^2$

Effortless Math Education

Chapter 12: Statistics

Math Topics that you'll learn in this Chapter:

- ✓ Mean, Median,
- ✓ Mode and Range
- ✓ Pie Graph
- ✓ Probability Problems
- ✓ Permutations and Combinations

107

Mean and Median

✎ *Find Mean and Median of the Given Data.*

1) 8, 12, 5, 3, 2

2) 3, 6, 3, 7, 4, 13

3) 13, 5, 1, 7, 9

4) 6, 4, 2, 7, 3, 2

5) 6, 5, 7, 5, 7, 1, 11

6) 6, 1, 4, 4, 9, 2, 16

7) 12, 4, 1, 5, 9, 7, 7, 19

8) 18, 9, 5, 4, 9, 6, 12

9) 28, 25, 15, 16, 32, 44, 71

10) 10, 5, 1, 5, 4, 5, 8, 10

11) 18, 15, 30, 64, 42, 11

12) 44, 33, 56, 78, 41, 84

✎ *Solve.*

13) In a javelin throw competition, five athletics score **56, 58, 63, 57** and **61** meters. What are their Mean and Median? _____

14) Eva went to shop and bought **3** apples, **5** peaches, **8** bananas, **1** pineapple and **3** melons. What are the Mean and Median of her purchase?

_____

15) Bob has **12** black pen, **14** red pen, **15** green pens, **24** blue pens and **3** boxes of yellow pens. If the Mean and Median of the number of pens for each color are **16** and **15** respectively, what is the number of yellow pens in each box?

_____

Mode and Range

✏️ **Find Mode and Rage of the Given Data.**

1) $8, 2, 5, 9, 1, 2$

Mode: _____   Range: _____

2) $6, 6, 2, 3, 6, 3, 9, 12$

Mode: _____   Range: _____

3) $4, 4, 3, 9, 7, 9, 4, 6, 4$

Mode: _____   Range: _____

4) $12, 9, 2, 9, 3, 2, 9, 5$

Mode: _____   Range: _____

5) $9, 5, 9, 5, 8, 9, 8$

Mode: _____   Range: _____

6) $0, 1, 4, 10, 9, 2, 9, 1, 5, 1$

Mode: _____   Range: _____

7) $6, 5, 6, 9, 7, 7, 5, 4, 3, 5$

Mode: _____   Range: _____

8) $7, 5, 4, 9, 6, 7, 7, 5, 2$

Mode: _____   Range: _____

9) $2, 2, 5, 6, 2, 4, 7, 6, 4, 9$

Mode: _____   Range: _____

10) $7, 5, 2, 5, 4, 5, 8, 10$

Mode: _____   Range: _____

11) $4, 1, 5, 2, 2, 12, 18, 2$

Mode: _____   Range: _____

12) $6, 3, 5, 9, 6, 6, 3, 12$

Mode: _____   Range: _____

✏️ **Solve.**

13) A stationery sold 12 pencils, 36 red pens, 44 blue pens, 12 notebooks, 18 erasers, 34 rulers and 32 color pencils. What are the Mode and Range for the stationery sells?

Mode: _____   Range: _____

14) In an English test, eight students score $14, 13, 17, 11, 19, 20, 14$ and 15. What are their Mode and Range? _____

15) What is the range of the first 6 even numbers greater than 11? _____

bit.ly/2KO86gg

Find more at

Pie Graph

The circle graph below shows all Jason's expenses for last month. Jason spent $300 on his bills last month.

Answer following questions based on the Pie graph.

Jason's monthly expenses

1- How much did Jason spend on his car last month? _____

2- How much did Jason spend for foods last month? _____

3- How much did Jason spend on his rent last month? _____

4- What fraction is Jason's expenses for his bills and Car out of his total

expenses last month? _____

5- How much was Jason's total expenses last month? _____

Probability Problems

✎ *Solve.*

1) A number is chosen at random from **1** to **10**. Find the probability of selecting number **4** or smaller numbers. _____

2) Bag A contains **9** red marbles and **3** green marbles. Bag B contains **9** black marbles and **6** orange marbles. What is the probability of selecting a green marble at random from bag A? What is the probability of selecting a black marble at random from Bag B? _____ _____

3) A number is chosen at random from **1** to **50**. What is the probability of selecting multiples of **10**. _____

4) A card is chosen from a well-shuffled deck of **52** cards. What is the probability that the card will be a king OR a queen? (The deck includes **13** of each suit clubs, diamonds, hearts, and spades) _____

5) A number is chosen at random from **1** to **10**. What is the probability of selecting a multiple of **3**?_____

A spinner, numbered **1–8**, is spun once. What is the probability of spinning...

6) an EVEN number? _____   7) a multiple of 3? _____

8) a PRIME number? _____   9) number 9? _____

bit.ly/3phwk1p

Find more at

Combinations and Permutations

✍ *Calculate the value of each.*

1) 4! = _____

2) 4! × 3! = _____

3) 5! = _____

4) 6! + 3! = _____

5) 7! = _____

6) 8! = _____

7) 4! + 4! = _____

8) 4! − 3! = _____

✍ *Solve each word problems.*

9) Susan is baking cookies. She uses sugar, flour, butter, and eggs. How many different orders of ingredients can she try? _____

10) Jason is planning for his vacation. He wants to go to museum, watch a movie, go to the beach, and play volleyball. How many different ways of ordering are there for him? _____

11) How many 5-digit numbers can be named using the digits 1, 2, 3, 4, and 5 without repetition? _____

12) In how many ways can 5 boys be arranged in a straight line? _____

13) In how many ways can 4 athletes be arranged in a straight line? _____

14) A professor is going to arrange her 7 students in a straight line. In how many ways can she do this? _____

15) How many code symbols can be formed with the letters for the word WHITE? _____

16) In how many ways a team of 8 basketball players can to choose a captain and co-captain? _____

Answers – Chapter 12

Mean and Median

1) Mean: 6, Median: 5
2) Mean: 6, Median: 5
3) Mean: 7, Median: 7
4) Mean: 4, Median: 3.5
5) Mean: 6, Median: 6

6) Mean: 6, Median: 4
7) Mean: 8, Median: 7
8) Mean: 9, Median: 9
9) Mean: 33, Median: 28
10) Mean: 6, Median: 5

11) Mean: 30, Median: 24
12) Mean: 56, Median: 50
13) Mean: 59, Median: 58
14) Mean: 4, Median: 3
15) 5

Mode and Range

1) Mode: 2, Range: 8
2) Mode: 6, Range: 10
3) Mode: 4, Range: 6
4) Mode: 9, Range: 10
5) Mode: 9, Range: 4

6) Mode: 1, Range: 10
7) Mode: 5, Range: 6
8) Mode: 7, Range: 7
9) Mode: 2, Range: 7
10) Mode: 5, Range: 8

11) Mode: 2, Range: 17
12) Mode: 6, Range: 9
13) Mode: 12, Range: 32
14) Mode: 14, Range: 9
15) 10

Pie Graph

1) $550
2) $250
3) $700

4) $\frac{17}{50}$
5) $2,500

Probability Problems

1) $\frac{2}{5}$
2) $\frac{1}{4}, \frac{3}{5}$
3) $\frac{1}{10}$

4) $\frac{2}{13}$
5) $\frac{3}{10}$
6) $\frac{1}{2}$

7) $\frac{1}{4}$
8) $\frac{1}{2}$
9) 0

Combinations and Permutations

1) 24
2) 144
3) 120
4) 726
5) 5,040
6) 40,320

7) 48
8) 18
9) 24
10) 24
11) 120
12) 120

13) 24
14) 5,040
15) 120
16) 56

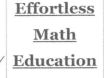

Chapter 13: Functions Operations

Math Topics that you'll learn in this Chapter:

- ✓ Function Notation and Evaluation
- ✓ Adding and Subtracting Functions
- ✓ Multiplying and Dividing Functions
- ✓ Composition of Functions

115

Function Notation and Evaluation

✏️ **Evaluate each function.**

1) $f(x) = x - 3$, find $f(-2)$

_____

2) $g(x) = x + 5$, find $g(6)$

_____

3) $h(x) = x + 8$, find $h(2)$

_____

4) $f(x) = -x - 7$, find $f(5)$

_____

5) $f(x) = 2x - 7$, find $f(-1)$

_____

6) $w(x) = -2 - 4x$, find $w(5)$

_____

7) $g(n) = 6n - 3$, find $g(-2)$

_____

8) $h(x) = -8x + 12$, find $h(3)$

_____

9) $k(n) = 14 - 3n$, find $k(3)$

_____

10) $g(x) = 4x - 4$, find $g(-2)$

_____

11) $k(n) = 8n - 7$, find $k(4)$

_____

12) $w(n) = -2n + 14$, find $w(5)$

_____

13) $h(x) = 5x - 18$, find $h(8)$

_____

14) $g(n) = 2n^2 + 2$, find $g(5)$

_____

15) $f(x) = 3x^2 - 13$, find $f(2)$

_____

16) $g(n) = 5n^2 + 7$, find $g(-3)$

_____

17) $h(n) = 5n^2 - 10$, find $h(4)$

_____

18) $g(x) = -3x^2 - 6x$, find $g(2)$

_____

19) $k(n) = 4n^3 + n$, find $k(-5)$

_____

20) $f(x) = -3x + 10$, find $f(3x)$

_____

21) $k(a) = 4a + 9$, find $k(a - 1)$

_____

22) $h(x) = 8x + 4$, find $h(5x)$

_____

Adding and Subtracting Functions

✎ **Perform the indicated operation.**

1) $f(x) = x + 4$

   $g(x) = 2x + 5$

   Find $(f - g)(2)$

   _____

2) $g(x) = x - 2$

   $f(x) = -x - 6$

   Find $(g - f)(-2)$

   _____

3) $h(t) = 4t + 4$

   $g(t) = 3t + 2$

   Find $(h + g)(-1)$

   _____

4) $g(a) = 5a - 7$

   $f(a) = a^2 + 3$

   Find $(g + f)(2)$

   _____

5) $g(x) = 4x - 5$

   $f(x) = 6x^2 + 5$

   Find $(g - f)(-2)$

   _____

6) $h(x) = x^2 + 3$

   $g(x) = -4x + 1$

   Find $(h + g)(4)$

   _____

7) $f(x) = -3x - 9$

   $g(x) = x^2 + 5$

   Find $(f - g)(6)$

   _____

8) $h(n) = -4n^2 + 9$

   $g(n) = 5n + 6$

   Find $(h - g)(5)$

   _____

9) $g(x) = 4x^2 - 3x - 1$

   $f(x) = 6x + 10$

   Find $(g - f)(a)$

   _____

10) $g(t) = -6t - 7$

   $f(t) = -t^2 + 3t + 15$

   Find $(g + f)(t)$

   _____

Multiplying and Dividing Functions

✎ *Perform the indicated operation.*

1) $g(x) = x + 6$

     $f(x) = x + 4$
     Find $(g.f)(2)$

_____

2) $f(x) = 3x$

     $h(x) = -x + 5$
     Find $(f.h)(-2)$

_____

3) $g(a) = a + 5$

     $h(a) = 2a - 4$
     Find $(g.h)(4)$

_____

4) $f(x) = 3x + 2$

     $h(x) = 2x - 3$
     Find $(\frac{f}{h})(2)$

_____

5) $f(x) = a^2 - 2$

     $g(x) = -4 + 3a$
     Find $(\frac{f}{g})(2)$

_____

6) $g(a) = 4a + 6$

     $f(a) = 2a - 8$
     Find $(\frac{g}{f})(3)$

_____

7) $g(t) = t^2 + 6$

     $h(t) = 2t - 3$
     Find $(g.h)(-3)$

_____

8) $g(x) = x^2 + 3x + 4$

     $h(x) = 2x + 6$
     Find $(g.h)(2)$

_____

9) $g(a) = 2a^2 - 5a + 1$

     $f(a) = 2a^3 - 6$
     Find $(\frac{g}{f})(4)$

_____

10) $g(x) = -3x^2 + 4 - 2x$

     $f(x) = x^2 - 5$
     Find $(g.f)(3)$

_____

Composition of Functions

Using $f(x) = x + 6$ and $g(x) = 3x$, find:

1) $f(g(1)) = \underline{\quad}$

2) $f(g(-1)) = \underline{\quad}$

3) $g(f(-3)) = \underline{\quad}$

4) $g(f(4)) = \underline{\quad}$

5) $f(g(2)) = \underline{\quad}$

6) $g(f(3)) = \underline{\quad}$

Using $f(x) = 2x + 5$ and $g(x) = x - 2$, find:

7) $g(f(2)) = \underline{\quad}$

8) $g(f(-2)) = \underline{\quad}$

9) $f(g(5)) = \underline{\quad}$

10) $f(f(4)) = \underline{\quad}$

11) $g(f(3)) = \underline{\quad}$

12) $g(f(-3)) = \underline{\quad}$

Using $f(x) = 4x - 2$ and $g(x) = x - 5$, find:

13) $g(f(-2)) = \underline{\quad}$

14) $f(f(4)) = \underline{\quad}$

15) $f(g(5)) = \underline{\quad}$

16) $f(f(3)) = \underline{\quad}$

17) $g(f(-3)) = \underline{\quad}$

18) $g(g(6)) = \underline{\quad}$

Using $f(x) = 6x + 2$ and $g(x) = 2x - 3$, find:

19) $f(g(-3)) = \underline{\quad}$

20) $g(f(5)) = \underline{\quad}$

21) $f(g(4)) = \underline{\quad}$

22) $f(f(3)) = \underline{\quad}$

bit.ly/2WHBkAg

Answers – Chapter 13

Function Notation and Evaluation

1) -5
2) 11
3) 10
4) -12
5) -9
6) -22
7) -15
8) -12

9) 5
10) -12
11) 25
12) 4
13) 22
14) 52
15) -1
16) 52

17) 70
18) -24
19) -505
20) $-9x + 10$
21) $4a + 5$
22) $40x + 4$

Adding and Subtracting Functions

1) -3
2) 0
3) -1
4) 10

5) -42
6) 4
7) -68
8) -122

9) $4a^2 - 9a - 11$
10) $-t^2 - 3t + 8$

Multiplying and Dividing Functions

1) 48
2) -42
3) 36
4) 8

5) 1
6) -9
7) -135
8) 140

9) $\frac{13}{122}$
10) -116

Composition of Functions

1) $f\big(g(1)\big) = 9$
2) $f\big(g(-1)\big) = 3$
3) $g\big(f(-3)\big) = 9$
4) $g\big(f(4)\big) = 30$
5) $f\big(g(2)\big) = 12$
6) $g\big(f(3)\big) = 27$
7) $g\big(f(2)\big) = 7$
8) $g\big(f(-2)\big) = -1$

9) $f\big(g(5)\big) = 11$
10) $f\big(f(4)\big) = 31$
11) $g\big(f(3)\big) = 9$
12) $g\big(f(-3)\big) = -3$
13) $g\big(f(-2)\big) = -15$
14) $f\big(f(4)\big) = 54$
15) $f\big(g(5)\big) = -2$
16) $f\big(f(3)\big) = 38$

17) $g\big(f(-3)\big) = -19$
18) $g\big(g(6)\big) = -4$
19) $f\big(g(-3)\big) = -52$
20) $g\big(f(5)\big) = 61$
21) $f\big(g(4)\big) = 32$
22) $f\big(f(3)\big) = 122$

Effortless Math Education

Chapter 14: Quadratic

Math Topics that you'll learn in this Chapter:

- ✓ Solving Quadratic Equations
- ✓ Graphing Quadratic Functions
- ✓ Solve Quadratic Inequalities
- ✓ Graphing Quadratic Inequalities

Solving Quadratic Equations

✍ **Solve each equation by factoring or using the quadratic formula.**

1) $(x + 2)(x - 7) = 0$

2) $(x + 3)(x + 5) = 0$

3) $(x - 9)(x + 4) = 0$

4) $(x - 7)(x - 5) = 0$

5) $(x + 4)(x + 8) = 0$

6) $(5x + 7)(x + 4) = 0$

7) $(2x + 5)(4x + 3) = 0$

8) $(3x + 4)(x + 2) = 0$

9) $(6x + 3)(2x + 4) = 0$

10) $(9x + 3)(x + 6) = 0$

11) $x^2 = 2x$

12) $x^2 - 6 = x$

13) $2x^2 + 4 = 6x$

14) $-x^2 - 6 = 5x$

15) $x^2 + 8x = 9$

16) $x^2 + 10x = 24$

17) $x^2 + 7x = -10$

18) $x^2 + 12x = -32$

19) $x^2 + 11x = -28$

20) $x^2 + x - 20 = 2x$

21) $x^2 + 8x = -15$

22) $7x^2 - 14x = -7$

23) $10x^2 = 27x - 18$

24) $7x^2 - 6x + 3 = 3$

25) $2x^2 - 14 = -3x$

26) $10x^2 - 26x = -12$

27) $15x^2 + 80 = -80x$

28) $x^2 + 15x = -56$

29) $6x^2 - 18x - 18 = 6$

30) $2x^2 + 6x - 24 = 12$

31) $2x^2 - 22x + 38 = -10$

32) $-4x^2 - 8x - 3 = -3 - 5x^2$

Graphing Quadratic Functions

✒️ *Sketch the graph of each function. Identify the vertex and axis of symmetry.*

1) $y = 3(x + 1)^2 + 2$

2) $y = -(x - 2)^2 - 4$

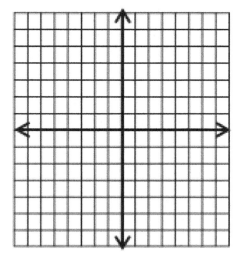

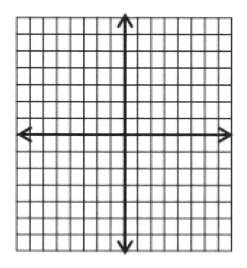

3) $y = 2(x - 3)^2 + 8$

4) $y = x^2 - 8x + 19$

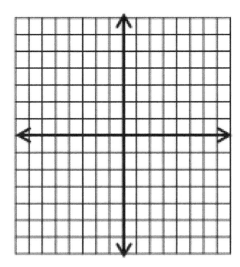

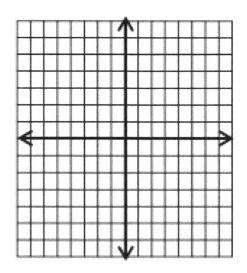

Quadratic Inequalities

✍️ *Solve each quadratic inequality.*

1) $x^2 - 1 < 0$

2) $-x^2 - 5x + 6 > 0$

3) $x^2 - 5x - 6 < 0$

4) $x^2 + 4x - 5 > 0$

5) $x^2 - 2x - 3 \geq 0$

6) $x^2 > 5x + 6$

7) $-x^2 - 12x - 11 \leq 0$

8) $x^2 - 2x - 8 \geq 0$

9) $x^2 - 5x - 6 \geq 0$

10) $x^2 + 7x + 10 < 0$

11) $x^2 + 9x + 20 > 0$

12) $x^2 - 8x + 16 > 0$

13) $x^2 - 8x + 12 \leq 0$

14) $x^2 - 11x + 30 \leq 0$

15) $x^2 - 12x + 27 \geq 0$

16) $x^2 - 16x + 64 \geq 0$

17) $x^2 - 36 \leq 0$

18) $x^2 - 13x + 36 \geq 0$

19) $x^2 + 15x + 36 \leq 0$

20) $4x^2 - 6x - 9 > x^2$

21) $5x^2 - 15x + 10 < 0$

22) $3x^2 - 5x \geq 4x^2 + 6$

23) $4x^2 - 12 > 3x^2 + x$

24) $x^2 - 2x \geq x^2 - 6x + 12$

25) $2x^2 + 2x - 8 > x^2$

26) $4x^2 + 20x - 11 < 0$

27) $-9x^2 + 29x - 6 \geq 0$

28) $-8x^2 + 6x - 1 \leq 0$

29) $12x^2 + 10x - 12 > 0$

30) $18x^2 + 23x + 5 \leq 0$

31) $17x^2 + 15x - 2 \geq 0$

32) $3x^2 + 7x \leq 5x^2 + 3x - 6$

Graphing Quadratic Inequalities

✎ *Sketch the graph of each quadratic inequality.*

1) $y < -2x^2$

2) $y > 3x^2$

3) $y \geq -3x^2$

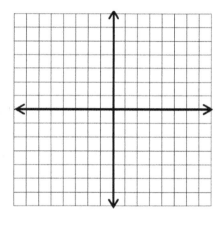
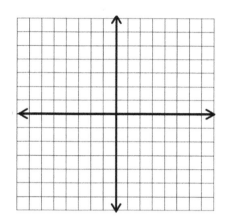
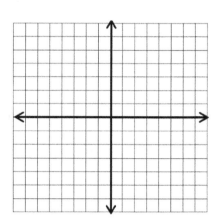

4) $y < x^2 + 1$

5) $y \geq -x^2 + 2$

6) $y \leq x^2 - 2x - 3$

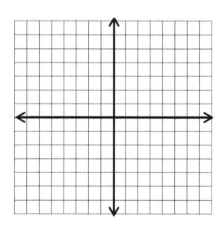
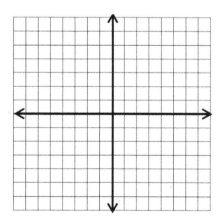
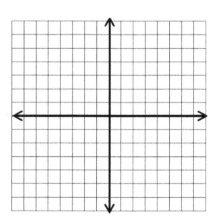

Answers – Chapter 14

Solving quadratic equations

1) $\{-2, 7\}$
2) $\{-3, -5\}$
3) $\{9, -4\}$
4) $\{7, 5\}$
5) $\{-4, -8\}$
6) $\{-\frac{7}{5}, -4\}$
7) $\{-\frac{5}{2}, -\frac{3}{4}\}$
8) $\{-\frac{4}{3}, -2\}$
9) $\{-\frac{1}{2}, -2\}$
10) $\{-\frac{1}{3}, -6\}$

11) $\{2, 0\}$
12) $\{3, -2\}$
13) $\{2, 1\}$
14) $\{-3, -2\}$
15) $\{1, -9\}$
16) $\{2, -12\}$
17) $\{-2, -5\}$
18) $\{-4, -8\}$
19) $\{-4, -7\}$
20) $\{5, -4\}$
21) $\{-5, -3\}$
22) $\{1\}$

23) $\{\frac{6}{5}, \frac{3}{2}\}$
24) $\{\frac{6}{7}, 0\}$
25) $\{-\frac{7}{2}, 2\}$
26) $\{\frac{3}{5}, 2\}$
27) $\{-\frac{4}{3}, -4\}$
28) $\{-8, -7\}$
29) $\{4, -1\}$
30) $\{3, -6\}$
31) $\{3, 8\}$
32) $\{8, 0\}$

Graphing quadratic functions

1) $(-1, 2), x = -1$

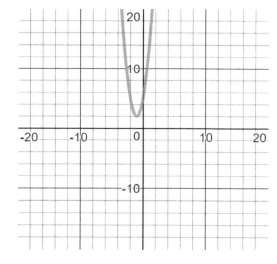

2) $(2, -4), x = 2$

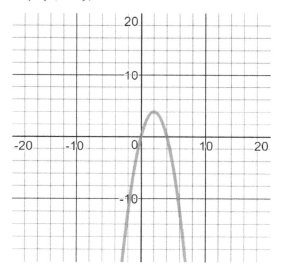

3) $(3, 8), x = 3$

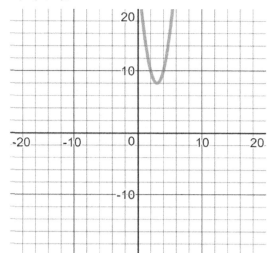

4) $(4, 3), x = 4$

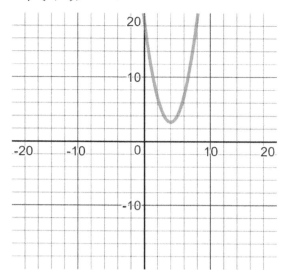

Solve quadratic inequalities

1) $-1 < x < 1$
2) $-6 < x < 1$
3) $-1 < x < 6$
4) $x < -5 \ or \ x > 1$
5) $x \leq -1 \ or \ x \geq 3$
6) $x < -1 \ or \ x > 6$
7) $x \leq -11 \ or \ x \geq -1$
8) $x \leq -2 \ or \ x \geq 4$
9) $x \leq -1 \ or \ x \geq 6$
10) $-5 < x < -2$
11) $x < -5 \ or \ x > -4$

12) $x < 4 \ or \ x > 4$
13) $2 \leq x \leq 6$
14) $5 \leq x \leq 6$
15) $x \leq 3 \ or \ x \geq 9$
16) *all real numbers*
17) $-6 \leq x \leq 6$
18) $x \leq 4 \ or \ x \geq 9$
19) $-12 \leq x \leq -3$
20) $x < -1 \ or \ x > 3$
21) $1 < x < 2$
22) $-3 \leq x \leq -2$
23) $x < -3 \ or \ x > 4$

24) $x \geq 3$
25) $x < -4 \ or \ x > 2$
26) $-\frac{11}{2} < x < \frac{1}{2}$
27) $\frac{2}{9} \leq x \leq 3$
28) $x \leq \frac{1}{4} \ or \ x \geq \frac{1}{2}$
29) $x < -1.5 \ or \ x > \frac{2}{3}$
30) $-1 \leq x \leq -\frac{5}{18}$
31) $x \leq -1 \ or \ x \geq \frac{2}{17}$
32) $x \leq -1 \ or \ x \geq 3$

Effortless Math Education

Graphing Quadratic Inequalities

1) $y < -2x^2$

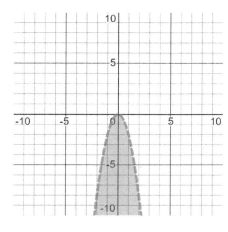

2) $y > 3x^2$

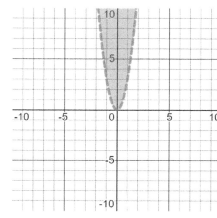

3) $y \geq -3x^2$

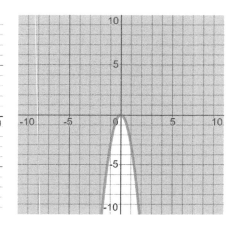

4) $y < x^2 + 1$

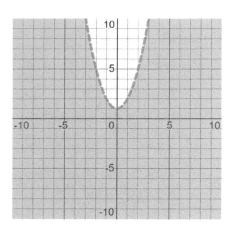

5) $y \geq -x^2 + 2$

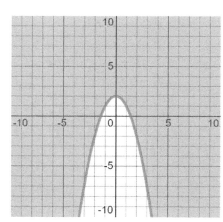

6) $y \leq x^2 - 2x - 3$

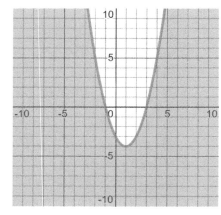

Chapter 15: Complex Numbers

Math Topics that you'll learn in this Chapter:

- ✓ Adding and Subtracting Complex Numbers
- ✓ Multiplying and Dividing Complex Numbers
- ✓ Rationalizing Imaginary Denominators

Adding and Subtracting Complex Numbers

✍ **Simplify.**

1) $(2i) - (i) =$

2) $(2i) + (2i) =$

3) $(i) + (3i) =$

4) $(-2i) - (6i) =$

5) $(5i) + (4i) =$

6) $(3i) - (-7i) =$

7) $(-6i) + (-9i) =$

8) $(15i) - (7i) =$

9) $(-12i) - (5i) =$

10) $(2i) + (2 + 3i) =$

11) $(2 - 4i) + (-i) =$

12) $(-3i) + (3 + 5i) =$

13) $3 + (2 - 4i) =$

14) $(-5i) - (-5 + 2i) =$

15) $(5 + 3i) - (-4i) =$

16) $(8 + 5i) + (-7i) =$

17) $(9i) - (-6i + 10) =$

18) $(12i + 8) + (-7i) =$

19) $(13i) - (17 + 3i) =$

20) $(3 + 5i) + (8 + 3i) =$

21) $(8 - 3i) + (4 + i) =$

22) $(10 + 9i) + (6 + 8i) =$

23) $(-3 + 6i) - (-9 - i) =$

24) $(-5 + 15i) - (-3 + 3i) =$

25) $(-14 + i) - (-12 - 11i) =$

26) $(-18 - 3i) + (11 + 5i) =$

27) $(-11 - 9i) - (-9 - 3i) =$

28) $-8 + (2i) + (-8 + 6i) =$

29) $12 - (5i) + (4 - 14i) =$

30) $-2 + (-8 - 7i) - 9 =$

31) $(-12i) + (2 - 6i) + 10 =$

32) $(-8i) - (8 - 5i) + 6i =$

Multiplying and Dividing Complex Numbers

✍ **Simplify.**

1) $(5i)(-i) =$

2) $(-4i)(5i) =$

3) $(i)(7i)(-i) =$

4) $(3i)(-4i) =$

5) $(-2 - i)(4 + i) =$

6) $(2 - 2i)^2 =$

7) $(4 - 3i)(6 - 6i) =$

8) $(5 + 4i)^2 =$

9) $(4i)(-i)(2 - 5i) =$

10) $(2 - 8i)(3 - 5i) =$

11) $(-5 + 9i)(3 + 5i) =$

12) $(7 + 3i)(7 + 8i) =$

13) $2(3i) - (5i)(-8 + 5i) =$

14) $\frac{5}{-10i} =$

15) $\frac{4 - 3i}{-4i} =$

16) $\frac{5 + 9i}{i} =$

17) $\frac{12i}{-9 + 3i} =$

18) $\frac{-3 - 10i}{5i} =$

19) $\frac{9i}{3 - i} =$

20) $\frac{2 + 4i}{14 + 4i} =$

21) $\frac{5 + 6i}{-1 + 8i} =$

22) $\frac{-8 - i}{-4 - 6i} =$

23) $\frac{-1 + 5i}{-8 - 7i} =$

24) $\frac{-2 - 9i}{-2 + 7i} =$

25) $\frac{4 + i}{2 - 5i} =$

Rationalizing Imaginary Denominators

✎ **Simplify.**

1) $\dfrac{-2}{-2i} =$

2) $\dfrac{-1}{-9i} =$

3) $\dfrac{-8}{-5i} =$

4) $\dfrac{-5}{-i} =$

5) $\dfrac{3}{5i} =$

6) $\dfrac{6}{-4i} =$

7) $\dfrac{6}{-7i} =$

8) $\dfrac{-10}{3i} =$

9) $\dfrac{a}{bi} =$

10) $\dfrac{10-10i}{-5i} =$

11) $\dfrac{4-9i}{-6i} =$

12) $\dfrac{6+8i}{9i} =$

13) $\dfrac{8i}{-1+3i} =$

14) $\dfrac{5i}{-2-6i} =$

15) $\dfrac{-10-5i}{-6+6i} =$

16) $\dfrac{-5-9i}{9+8i} =$

17) $\dfrac{-5-3i}{7-10i} =$

18) $\dfrac{-1+i}{-5i} =$

19) $\dfrac{-6-i}{i} =$

20) $\dfrac{-4-i}{9+5i} =$

21) $\dfrac{-3+i}{-2i} =$

22) $\dfrac{-6-i}{-1+6i} =$

23) $\dfrac{-9-3i}{-3+3i} =$

24) $\dfrac{4i+1}{-1+3i} =$

Answers – Chapter 15

Adding and Subtracting Complex Numbers

1) i
2) $4i$
3) $4i$
4) $-8i$
5) $9i$
6) $10i$
7) $-15i$
8) $8i$
9) $-17i$
10) $2 + 5i$
11) $2 - 5i$

12) $3 + 2i$
13) $5 - 4i$
14) $5 - 7i$
15) $5 + 7i$
16) $8 - 2i$
17) $10 + 15i$
18) $8 + 5i$
19) $-17 + 10i$
20) $11 + 8i$
21) $12 - 2i$
22) $16 + 17i$

23) $6 + 7i$
24) $-2 + 12i$
25) $-2 + 12i$
26) $-7 + 2i$
27) $-2 - 6i$
28) $-16 + 8i$
29) $16 - 19i$
30) $-19 - 7i$
31) $12 - 18i$
32) $-8 + 3i$

Multiplying and Dividing Complex Numbers

1) 5
2) 20
3) $7i$
4) 12
5) $-7 - 6i$
6) $-8i$
7) $6 - 42i$
8) $9 + 40i$
9) $8 - 20i$
10) $-34 - 34i$
11) $-60 + 2i$

12) $25 + 77i$
13) $25 + 46i$
14) $\dfrac{i}{2}$
15) $\dfrac{3}{4} + i$
16) $9 - 5i$
17) $\dfrac{2}{5} - \dfrac{6}{5}i$
18) $-2 + \dfrac{3}{5}i$
19) $-\dfrac{9}{10} + \dfrac{27}{10}i$

20) $\dfrac{11}{53} + \dfrac{12}{53}i$
21) $\dfrac{43}{65} - \dfrac{46}{65}i$
22) $\dfrac{19}{26} + \dfrac{11}{13}i$
23) $-\dfrac{27}{113} - \dfrac{47}{113}i$
24) $-\dfrac{59}{53} + \dfrac{32}{53}i$
25) $\dfrac{3}{29} + \dfrac{22}{29}i$

Rationalizing Imaginary Denominators

1) $-i$
2) $-\dfrac{1}{9}i$
3) $\dfrac{-8}{5}i$
4) $-5i$
5) $-\dfrac{3}{5}i$
6) $\dfrac{3}{2}i$

7) $\dfrac{6}{7}i$
8) $\dfrac{10}{3}i$
9) $-\dfrac{a}{b}i$
10) $2 + 2i$
11) $\dfrac{2}{3} + \dfrac{3}{2}i$
12) $\dfrac{6}{91} + \dfrac{8}{91}i$

13) $\dfrac{12}{5} - \dfrac{4}{5}i$
14) $-\dfrac{3}{4} - \dfrac{1}{4}i$
15) $\dfrac{5}{12} + \dfrac{5}{4}i$
16) $-\dfrac{117}{145} - \dfrac{41}{145}i$
17) $-\dfrac{5}{149} - \dfrac{71}{149}i$

Effortless
Math
Education

18) $-\frac{1}{5} - \frac{1}{5}i$

19) $-1 + 6i$

20) $-\frac{41}{106} + \frac{11}{106}i$

21) $-\frac{1}{2} - \frac{3}{2}i$

22) i

23) $1 + 2i$

24) $\frac{11}{10} - \frac{7}{10}i$

Chapter 16: Radical Expressions

Math Topics that you'll learn in this Chapter:

- ✓ Simplifying Radical Expressions
- ✓ Adding and Subtracting Radical Expressions
- ✓ Multiplying Radical Expressions
- ✓ Simplifying Radical Expressions Involving Fractions
- ✓ Domain and Range of Radical Functions
- ✓ Solving Radical Equations

135

Simplifying Radical Expressions

✎ **Simplify.**

1) $\sqrt{35x^2} =$

2) $\sqrt{90x^2} =$

3) $\sqrt[3]{8a} =$

4) $\sqrt{100x^3} =$

5) $\sqrt{125a} =$

6) $\sqrt[3]{88w^3} =$

7) $\sqrt{80x} =$

8) $\sqrt{216v} =$

9) $\sqrt[3]{125x}$

10) $\sqrt{64x^5} =$

11) $\sqrt{4x^2} =$

12) $\sqrt[3]{54a^2}$

13) $\sqrt{405} =$

14) $\sqrt{512p^3} =$

15) $\sqrt{216m^4} =$

16) $\sqrt{264x^3y^3} =$

17) $\sqrt{49x^3y^3} =$

18) $\sqrt{16a^4b^3} =$

19) $\sqrt{20x^3y^3} =$

20) $\sqrt[3]{216yx^3} =$

21) $3\sqrt{75x^2} =$

22) $5\sqrt{80x^2} =$

23) $\sqrt[3]{256x^2y^3} =$

24) $\sqrt[3]{343x^4y^2} =$

25) $4\sqrt{125a} =$

26) $\sqrt[3]{625xy} =$

27) $2\sqrt{8x^2y^3r} =$

28) $4\sqrt{36x^2y^3z^4} =$

29) $2\sqrt[3]{512x^3y^4} =$

30) $5\sqrt{64a^2b^3c^5} =$

31) $2\sqrt[3]{125x^6y^{12}} =$

Adding and Subtracting Radical Expressions

✎ **Simplify.**

1) $\sqrt{3} + \sqrt{27} =$

2) $3\sqrt{8} + 3\sqrt{2} =$

3) $4\sqrt{3} - 2\sqrt{12} =$

4) $3\sqrt{18} - 2\sqrt{2} =$

5) $2\sqrt{45} - 2\sqrt{5} =$

6) $-\sqrt{12} - 5\sqrt{3} =$

7) $-4\sqrt{2} - 5\sqrt{32} =$

8) $5\sqrt{10} + 2\sqrt{40} =$

9) $4\sqrt{12} - 3\sqrt{27} =$

10) $-3\sqrt{2} + 4\sqrt{18} =$

11) $-10\sqrt{7} + 6\sqrt{28} =$

12) $5\sqrt{3} - \sqrt{27} =$

13) $-\sqrt{12} + 3\sqrt{3} =$

14) $-3\sqrt{6} - \sqrt{54} =$

15) $3\sqrt{8} + 3\sqrt{2} =$

16) $2\sqrt{12} - 3\sqrt{27} =$

17) $\sqrt{50} - \sqrt{32} =$

18) $4\sqrt{8} - 6\sqrt{2} =$

19) $-4\sqrt{12} + 12\sqrt{108} =$

20) $2\sqrt{45} - 2\sqrt{5} =$

21) $7\sqrt{18} - 3\sqrt{2} =$

22) $-12\sqrt{35} + 7\sqrt{140} =$

23) $-6\sqrt{19} - 3\sqrt{76} =$

24) $-\sqrt{54x} - 3\sqrt{6x} =$

25) $\sqrt{5y^2} + y\sqrt{45} =$

26) $\sqrt{8mn^2} + 2n\sqrt{18m} =$

27) $-8\sqrt{27a} - 5\sqrt{3a} =$

28) $-4\sqrt{7ab} - \sqrt{28ab} =$

29) $\sqrt{27a^2b} + a\sqrt{12b} =$

30) $3\sqrt{6a^3} - 2\sqrt{24a^3} + 2a\sqrt{54a} =$

Multiplying Radical Expressions

✎ *Simplify.*

1) $\sqrt{5} \times \sqrt{5} =$

2) $\sqrt{5} \times \sqrt{10} =$

3) $\sqrt{2} \times \sqrt{18} =$

4) $\sqrt{14} \times \sqrt{21} =$

5) $\sqrt{5} \times -4\sqrt{20} =$

6) $3\sqrt{12} \times \sqrt{6} =$

7) $5\sqrt{42} \times \sqrt{3} =$

8) $\sqrt{3} \times -\sqrt{25} =$

9) $\sqrt{99} \times \sqrt{48} =$

10) $5\sqrt{45} \times 3\sqrt{176} =$

11) $\sqrt{12}(3 + \sqrt{3}) =$

12) $\sqrt{23x^2} \times \sqrt{23x} =$

13) $-5\sqrt{12} \times - \sqrt{3} =$

14) $2\sqrt{20x^2} \times \sqrt{5x^2} =$

15) $\sqrt{12x^2} \times \sqrt{2x^3} =$

16) $-12\sqrt{7x} \times \sqrt{5x^3} =$

17) $-5\sqrt{9x^3} \times 6\sqrt{3x^2} =$

18) $-2\sqrt{12}(3 + \sqrt{12}) =$

19) $\sqrt{18x}\,(4 - \sqrt{6x}) =$

20) $\sqrt{3x}(6\sqrt{x^3} + \sqrt{27}) =$

21) $\sqrt{15r}\,(5 + \sqrt{5}) =$

22) $-5\sqrt{3x} \times 4\sqrt{6x^3} =$

23) $-2\sqrt{18x} \times 4\sqrt{2x}$

24) $-3\sqrt{5v^2}\,(-3\sqrt{15v}) =$

25) $(\sqrt{5} - \sqrt{3})(\sqrt{5} + \sqrt{3}) =$

26) $(-4\sqrt{6} + 2)(\sqrt{6} - 5) =$

27) $(2 - 2\sqrt{3})(-2 + \sqrt{3}) =$

28) $(11 - 4\sqrt{5})(6 - \sqrt{5}) =$

29) $(-2 - \sqrt{3x})(3 + \sqrt{3x}) =$

30) $(-2 + 3\sqrt{2r})(-2 + \sqrt{2r}) =$

31) $(-4\sqrt{2n} + 2)(-2\sqrt{2} - 4) =$

32) $(-1 + 2\sqrt{3})(2 - 3\sqrt{3x}) =$

Simplifying Radical Expressions Involving Fractions

✎ **Simplify.**

1) $\dfrac{\sqrt{5}}{\sqrt{3}} =$

2) $\dfrac{\sqrt{8}}{\sqrt{100}} =$

3) $\dfrac{\sqrt{2}}{2\sqrt{3}} =$

4) $\dfrac{4}{\sqrt{5}} =$

5) $\dfrac{2\sqrt{5r}}{\sqrt{m^3}} =$

6) $\dfrac{8\sqrt{3}}{\sqrt{k}} =$

7) $\dfrac{6\sqrt{14x^2}}{2\sqrt{18x}} =$

8) $\dfrac{\sqrt{7x^2y^2}}{\sqrt{5x^3y^2}} =$

9) $\dfrac{1}{1+\sqrt{2}} =$

10) $\dfrac{1-5\sqrt{a}}{\sqrt{11a}} =$

11) $\dfrac{\sqrt{a}}{\sqrt{a}+\sqrt{b}} =$

12) $\dfrac{1+\sqrt{2}}{3+\sqrt{5}} =$

13) $\dfrac{2+\sqrt{5}}{6-\sqrt{3}} =$

14) $\dfrac{5}{-3-3\sqrt{3}} =$

15) $\dfrac{2}{3+\sqrt{5}} =$

16) $\dfrac{\sqrt{7}-\sqrt{3}}{\sqrt{3}-\sqrt{7}} =$

17) $\dfrac{\sqrt{7}+\sqrt{5}}{\sqrt{5}+\sqrt{2}} =$

18) $\dfrac{3\sqrt{2}-\sqrt{7}}{4\sqrt{2}+\sqrt{5}} =$

19) $\dfrac{\sqrt{5}+2\sqrt{2}}{4-\sqrt{5}} =$

20) $\dfrac{5\sqrt{3}-3\sqrt{2}}{3\sqrt{2}-2\sqrt{3}} =$

21) $\dfrac{\sqrt{8a^5b^3}}{\sqrt{2ab^2}} =$

22) $\dfrac{6\sqrt{45x^3}}{3\sqrt{5x}} =$

Domain and Range of Radical Functions

✍ **Identify the domain and range of each function.**

1) $y = \sqrt{x + 2} - 3$

2) $y = \sqrt[3]{x - 1} - 1$

3) $y = \sqrt{x - 2} + 5$

4) $y = \sqrt[3]{(x + 1)} - 4$

5) $y = 3\sqrt{3x + 6} + 5$

6) $y = \sqrt[3]{(2x - 1)} - 4$

7) $y = 6\sqrt{3x^2 + 6} + 5$

8) $y = \sqrt[3]{(2x^2 - 2)} - 4$

9) $y = 4\sqrt{4x^3 + 32} - 1$

10) $y = \sqrt[3]{(4x + 8)} - 2x$

11) $y = 7\sqrt{-2(2x + 4)} + 1$

12) $y = \sqrt[5]{(4x^2 - 5)} - 2$

13) $y = 2x\sqrt{5x^4 + 6} - 2x$

14) $y = 6\sqrt[3]{(8x^6 + 2x + 8)} - 2$

✍ **Sketch the graph of each function.**

15) $y = \sqrt{x} + 8$

16) $y = 2\sqrt{x} - 4$

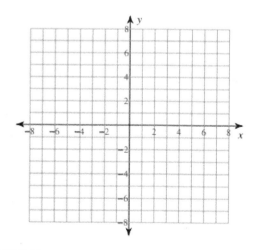

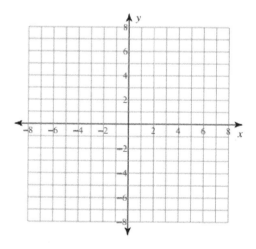

Solving Radical Equations

✎ **Solve each equation. Remember to check for extraneous solutions.**

1) $\sqrt{a} = 5$

2) $\sqrt{v} = 3$

3) $\sqrt{r} = 4$

4) $2 = 4\sqrt{x}$

5) $\sqrt{x+1} = 9$

6) $1 = \sqrt{x-5}$

7) $6 = \sqrt{r-2}$

8) $\sqrt{x-6} = 8$

9) $5 = \sqrt{x-3}$

10) $\sqrt{m+8} = 8$

11) $10\sqrt{9a} = 60$

12) $5\sqrt{3x} = 15$

13) $1 = \sqrt{3x-5}$

14) $\sqrt{12-x} = x$

15) $\sqrt{r+3} - 1 = 7$

16) $-12 = -6\sqrt{r+4}$

17) $20 = 2\sqrt{36v}$

18) $x = \sqrt{42-x}$

19) $\sqrt{110-a} = a$

20) $\sqrt{2n-12} = 2$

21) $\sqrt{3r-5} = r-3$

22) $\sqrt{-16+10x} = x$

23) $\sqrt{3x+12} = \sqrt{x+8}$

24) $\sqrt{v} = \sqrt{2v-6}$

25) $\sqrt{11-x} = \sqrt{x-7}$

26) $\sqrt{m+8} = \sqrt{3m+8}$

27) $\sqrt{2r+40} = \sqrt{-16-2r}$

28) $\sqrt{k+3} = \sqrt{1-k}$

29) $-10\sqrt{x-10} = -60$

30) $\sqrt{72-x} = \sqrt{\dfrac{x}{5}}$

Answers – Chapter 16

Simplifying radical expressions

1) $x\sqrt{35}$

2) $3x\sqrt{10}$

3) $2\sqrt[3]{a}$

4) $10x\sqrt{x}$

5) $5\sqrt{5a}$

6) $2w\sqrt[3]{11}$

7) $4\sqrt{5x}$

8) $6\sqrt{6v}$

9) $5\sqrt[3]{x}$

10) $8x^2\sqrt{x}$

11) $2x$

12) $3\sqrt[3]{2a^2}$

13) $9\sqrt{5}$

14) $16p\sqrt{2p}$

15) $6m^2\sqrt{6}$

16) $2x \cdot y\sqrt{66xy}$

17) $7xy\sqrt{xy}$

18) $4a^2b\sqrt{b}$

19) $2xy\sqrt{5xy}$

20) $6x\sqrt[3]{y}$

21) $15x\sqrt{3}$

22) $20x\sqrt{5}$

23) $16y\sqrt[3]{x^2}$

24) $7x\sqrt[3]{xy^2}$

25) $20\sqrt{5a}$

26) $5\sqrt[3]{5xy}$

27) $4xy\sqrt{2yr}$

28) $24\,x\,yz^2\sqrt{y}$

29) $16xy\sqrt[3]{y}$

30) $40abc^2\sqrt{bc}$

31) $10x^2y^4$

Adding and subtracting radical expressions

1) $4\sqrt{3}$

2) $9\sqrt{2}$

3) 0

4) $7\sqrt{2}$

5) $4\sqrt{5}$

6) $-7\sqrt{3}$

7) $-24\sqrt{2}$

8) $9\sqrt{10}$

9) $-\sqrt{3}$

10) $9\sqrt{2}$

11) $2\sqrt{7}$

12) $2\sqrt{3}$

13) $\sqrt{3}$

14) 0

15) $9\sqrt{2}$

16) $-5\sqrt{3}$

17) $\sqrt{2}$

18) $2\sqrt{2}$

19) $64\sqrt{3}$

20) $4\sqrt{5}$

21) $18\sqrt{2}$

22) $2\sqrt{35}$

23) $-12\sqrt{19}$

24) $-6\sqrt{6x}$

25) $4y\sqrt{5}$

26) $8n\sqrt{2m}$

27) $-29\sqrt{3a}$

28) $-8\sqrt{7ab}$

29) $5a\sqrt{3b}$

30) $5a\sqrt{6a}$

Multiplying radical expressions

1) 5

2) $5\sqrt{2}$

3) 6

4) $7\sqrt{6}$

5) -40

6) $18\sqrt{2}$

7) $15\sqrt{14}$

8) $-5\sqrt{3}$

9) $12\sqrt{33}$

10) $180\sqrt{55}$

11) $6\sqrt{3} + 6$

12) $23x\sqrt{x}$

13) 30

14) $20x^2$

15) $2x\sqrt{6x}$

16) $-12x^2\sqrt{35}$

17) $-90x^2\sqrt{3x}$

18) $-12\sqrt{3} - 24$

19) $6\sqrt{2x} - 6x\sqrt{3}$

20) $54x^2$

21) $5\sqrt{15r} + 3\sqrt{5r}$

22) $-60x^2\sqrt{2}$

23) $-48x$

24) $45v\sqrt{3v}$

25) 2

26) $22\sqrt{3} - 34$

27) $6\sqrt{3} - 10$

28) $86 - 35\sqrt{5}$

29) $-3x - 5\sqrt{3x} - 6$

30) $12r - 8\sqrt{2r} + 4$

31) $16\sqrt{n} + 16\sqrt{2n} - 4\sqrt{2} - 8$

32) $-2 + 3\sqrt{3x} + 4\sqrt{3} - 18\sqrt{x}$

Simplifying radical expressions involving fractions

1) $\frac{\sqrt{15}}{3}$

2) $\frac{\sqrt{2}}{5}$

3) $\frac{\sqrt{6}}{6}$

4) $\frac{4\sqrt{5}}{5}$

5) $\frac{2\sqrt{5mr}}{m^2}$

6) $\frac{8\sqrt{3k}}{k}$

7) $\sqrt{7x}$

8) $\frac{\sqrt{35x}}{5x}$

9) $-1 + \sqrt{2}$

10) $\frac{\sqrt{11a} - 5a\sqrt{11}}{11a}$

11) $\frac{a - \sqrt{ab}}{a - b}$

12) $\frac{3 - \sqrt{5} + 3\sqrt{2} - \sqrt{10}}{4}$

13) $\frac{12 + 2\sqrt{3} + 6\sqrt{5} + \sqrt{15}}{33}$

14) $\frac{5 - 5\sqrt{5}}{6}$

15) $-3 + \sqrt{5}$

16) -1

17) $\frac{\sqrt{35} - \sqrt{14} + 5 - \sqrt{10}}{3}$

18) $\frac{24 - 3\sqrt{10} - 4\sqrt{14} + \sqrt{35}}{27}$

19) $\frac{4\sqrt{5} + 5 + 8\sqrt{2} + 2\sqrt{10}}{11}$

20) $\frac{3\sqrt{6} + 4}{2}$

21) $2a^2\sqrt{b}$

22) $6x$

Domain and range of radical functions

1) domain: $x \geq -2$

   range: $y \geq -3$

2) domain: {all real numbers}

   range: {all real numbers}

3) domain: $x \geq 2$

   range: $y \geq 5$

4) domain: {all real numbers}

   range: {all real numbers}

5) domain: $x \geq -2$

   range: $y \geq 5$

6) domain: {all real numbers}

   range: {all real numbers}

7) domain: {all real numbers}

   range: {all real numbers}

8) domain: {all real numbers}

   range: {all real numbers}

9) domain: $x \geq -2$

   range: $y \geq -1$

10) domain: {all real numbers}

    range: {all real numbers}

11) domain: $x \leq -2$

    range: $y \geq 1$

12) domain: {all real numbers}

    range: {all real numbers}

13) domain: {all real numbers}

    range: {all real numbers}

14) domain: {all real numbers}

    range: {all real numbers}

15)

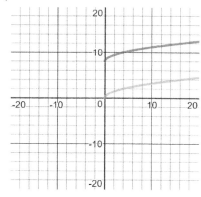

16)

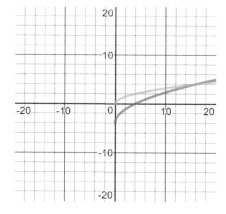

Solving radical equations

1) $\{25\}$

2) $\{9\}$

3) $\{16\}$

4) $\{\frac{1}{4}\}$

5) $\{80\}$

6) $\{6\}$

7) $\{38\}$

8) $\{70\}$

9) $\{28\}$

10) $\{56\}$

11) $\{4\}$

12) $\{3\}$

13) $\{2\}$

14) $\{3\}$

15) $\{61\}$

16) $\{0\}$

17) $\{\frac{25}{9}\}$

18) $\{6\}$

19) $\{10\}$

20) $\{8\}$

21) $\{4\}$

22) $\{2, 8\}$

23) $\{-2\}$

24) $\{6\}$

25) $\{9\}$

26) $\{0\}$

27) $\{-14\}$

28) $\{-1\}$

29) $\{46\}$

30) $\{60\}$

Effortless

Math

Education

Chapter 17: Logarithms

Math Topics that you'll learn in this Chapter:

- ✓ Evaluating Logarithms
- ✓ Properties of Logarithms
- ✓ Natural Logarithms
- ✓ Solving Logarithmic Equations

147

Evaluating Logarithms

✍ **Evaluate each logarithm.**

1) $\log_2 4 =$

2) $\log_2 8 =$

3) $\log_3 27 =$

4) $\log_3 9 =$

5) $\log_4 16 =$

6) $\log_2 32 =$

7) $\log_8 64 =$

8) $\log_2 \frac{1}{2} =$

9) $\log_2 \frac{1}{8} =$

10) $\log_3 \frac{1}{3} =$

11) $\log_4 \frac{1}{16} =$

12) $\log_3 \frac{1}{9} =$

13) $\log_7 \frac{1}{49} =$

14) $\log_{64} \frac{1}{4} =$

15) $\log_{625} 5 =$

16) $\log_2 \frac{1}{64} =$

17) $\log_4 \frac{1}{64} =$

18) $\log_{36} \frac{1}{6} =$

✍ **Circle the points which are on the graph of the given logarithmic functions.**

19) $y = 2\log_3(x + 1) + 2$ $(2, 4)$, $(8, 4)$, $(0, 3)$

20) $y = 3\log_3(3x) - 2$ $(3, 6)$, $(3, 4)$, $(\frac{1}{3}, 2)$

21) $y = -2\log_2 2(x - 1) + 1$ $(3, -3)$, $(2, 1)$, $(5, 5)$

22) $y = 4\log_4(4x) + 7$ $(1, 7)$, $(1, 11)$, $(4, 8)$

23) $y = -\log_2 2(x + 3) + 1$ $(-2, 0)$, $(1, 2)$, $(5, 3)$

24) $y = -\log_5(x - 3) + 8$ $(4, 8)$, $(8, 8)$, $(4, 4)$

25) $y = 3\log_4(x + 1) + 3$ $(3, 3)$, $(3, 6)$, $(0, 4)$

Properties of Logarithms

✎ **Expand each logarithm.**

1) $log\ (8 \times 5) =$

2) $log\ (9 \times 4) =$

3) $log\ (3 \times 7) =$

4) $log\ (\frac{3}{4}) =$

5) $log\ (\frac{5}{7}) =$

6) $log\ (\frac{2}{5})^3 =$

7) $log\ (2 \times 3^4) =$

8) $log\ (\frac{5}{7})^4 =$

9) $log\ \left(\frac{2^3}{7}\right) =$

10) $log\ (x \times y)^5 =$

11) $log\ (x^3 \times y \times z^4) =$

12) $log\ \left(\frac{u^4}{v}\right) =$

13) $log\ \left(\frac{x}{y^6}\right) =$

✎ **Condense each expression to a single logarithm.**

14) $log\ 2 - log\ 9 =$

15) $log\ 5 + log\ 3 =$

16) $5\ log\ 6 - 3\ log\ 4 =$

17) $4\ log\ 7 - 2\ log\ 9 =$

18) $3\ log\ 5 - log\ 14 =$

19) $7\ log\ 3 - 4log\ 4 =$

20) $log\ 7 - 2\ log\ 12 =$

21) $2log\ 5 + 3log\ 8 =$

22) $4log\ 3 + 5log\ 7 =$

23) $4\ log_5 a + 7\ log_5 b =$

24) $2log_3 x - 9\ log_3 y =$

25) $log_4 u - 6\ log_4 v =$

26) $4\ log_6 u + 8\ log_6 v =$

27) $4\ log_3 u - 20\ log_3 v =$

Natural Logarithms

✎ **Solve each equation for** x.

1) $e^x = 3$

2) $e^x = 4$

3) $e^x = 8$

4) $ln\ x = 6$

5) $ln\ (ln\ x) = 5$

6) $e^x = 9$

7) $ln(2x + 5) = 4$

8) $ln(2x - 1) = 1$

9) $ln(6x - 1) = 1$

10) $ln\ x = \frac{1}{2}$

11) $ln2x = e^2$

12) $ln\ x = ln\ 4 + ln\ 7$

13) $ln\ x = 2ln\ 4 + ln\ 5$

✎ **Evaluate without using a calculator.**

14) $ln\ 1 =$

15) $ln\ e^3 =$

16) $2 \ln e =$

17) $ln\ e^2 =$

18) $4ln\ e =$

19) $ln\left(\frac{1}{e}\right) =$

20) $e^{ln10} =$

21) $e^{3ln2} =$

22) $e^{5ln2} =$

23) $ln\ \sqrt{e} =$

✎ **Reduce the following expressions to simplest form.**

24) $e^{-2ln5+2ln3} =$

25) $e^{-ln\left(\frac{1}{e}\right)} =$

26) $2\ ln(e^3) =$

27) $ln(\frac{1}{e})^2 =$

28) $e^{ln2+3ln2} =$

29) $e^{ln\left(\frac{2}{e}\right)} =$

30) $5\ ln(1^{-e}) =$

31) $ln(\frac{1}{e})^{-3} =$

32) $ln\left(\frac{\sqrt{e}}{e}\right) =$

33) $e^{-2lne+2ln2} =$

34) $e^{ln\frac{1}{e}} =$

35) $3\ ln(e^e) =$

Solving Logarithmic Equations

 Find the value of the variables in each equation.

1) $2log_7 - 2x = 0$

2) $-log_5 7x = 2$

3) $\log x + 5 = 2$

4) $\log x - \log 4 = 3$

5) $\log x + \log 2 = 4$

6) $\log 10 + \log x = 1$

7) $\log x + \log 8 = \log 48$

8) $-3 \log_3(x-2) = -12$

9) $\log 6x = \log (x + 5)$

10) $\log (4k - 5) = \log (2k - 1)$

11) $\log(4p - 2) = \log(-5p + 5)$

12) $-10 + \log_3 (n + 3) = -10$

13) $\log_9(x + 2) = \log_9 (x^2 + 30)$

14) $\log_{12} (v^2 + 35) = \log_{12} (-2v - 1)$

15) $\log (16 + 2b) = \log (b^2 - 4b)$

16) $\log_9(x + 6) - \log_9 x = \log_9 2$

17) $\log_5 6 + \log_5 2x^2 = \log_5 48$

18) $\log_6(x + 1) - \log_6 x = \log_6 29$

 Find the value of x **in each natural logarithm equation.**

19) $\ln 2 - \ln(3x + 2) = 1$

20) $\ln(x - 3) - \ln(x - 5) = \ln 5$

21) $\ln e^4 - \ln(x + 1) = 1$

22) $\ln(2x - 1) - \ln(x - 5) = \ln 5$

23) $\ln 2x + \ln(3x - 4) = \ln 4x$

24) $\ln(4x - 2) - 4\ln(x - 5) = \ln 10$

25) $\ln (4x + 2) - \ln 1 = 5$

26) $\ln(x - 3) + \ln(x - 5) = \ln 2$

27) $\ln 2 + \ln(3x + 2) = 4$

28) $2 \ln 4x - \ln(x + 6) = 2 \ln 3x$

29) $\ln x^2 + \ln x^3 = \ln 1$

30) $\ln x^4 - \ln(x + 4) = 4 \ln x$

31) $2 \ln(x - 3) = \ln(x^2 - 6x + 9)$

32) $\ln(x^2 + 12) = \ln(6x + 4)$

33) $2 \ln x - 2\ln(x + 2) = 4\ln(x^2)$

34) $\ln(4x - 3) - \ln(2x - 4) = \ln 5$

35) $\ln 2 + 4 \ln(x + 2) = \ln 2$

36) $2\ln e^2 + \ln(2x - 1) = \ln 5 + 4$

Answers – Chapter 17

Evaluating Logarithms

1) 2
2) 3
3) 3
4) 2
5) 2
6) 5
7) 2
8) -1
9) -3

10) -1
11) -2
12) -2
13) -2
14) $-\frac{1}{3}$
15) -4
16) -6
17) -3

18) $-\frac{1}{2}$
19) $(2, 4)$
20) $(3, 4)$
21) $(3, -3)$
22) $(1, 11)$
23) $(-2, 1)$
24) $(4, 8)$
25) $(3, 6)$

Properties of Logarithms

1) $\log 8 + \log 5$
2) $\log 9 + \log 9$
3) $\log 3 + \log 7$
4) $\log 3 - \log 4$
5) $\log 5 - \log 7$
6) $3 \log 2 - 3 \log 5$
7) $\log 2 + 4 \log 3$
8) $4\log 5 - 4 \log 7$
9) $3 \log 2 - \log 7$
10) $5 \log x + 5 \log y$
11) $\log x + \log y + 4 \log z$

12) $4 \log u - \log v$
13) $\log x - 6 \log y$
14) $\log \frac{2}{9}$
15) $\log(5 . 3)$
16) $\log \frac{6^5}{4^3}$
17) $\log \frac{7^4}{9^2}$
18) $\log \frac{5^3}{14}$
19) $\log \frac{3^7}{4^4}$

20) $\log \frac{7}{12^2}$
21) $\log (5^2 8^3)$
22) $\log (3^4 7^5)$
23) $\log_5 (a^4 b^7)$
24) $\log_3 \frac{x^2}{y^9}$
25) $\log_4 \frac{u}{v^6}$
26) $\log_6 (u^4 \times v^8)$
27) $\log_3 \frac{u^4}{v^{20}}$

Natural Logarithms

1) $x = \ln 3$
2) $x = \ln 4, x = 2\ln (2)$
3) $x = \ln 8, x = 3\ln (2)$
4) $x = e^6$
5) $x = e^{e^5}$
6) $x = \ln 9, x = 2\ln (3)$
7) $x = \frac{e^4 - 5}{2}$
8) $x = \frac{e+1}{2}$

9) $x = \frac{e+1}{6}$
10) $x = \sqrt{e}$
11) $x = \frac{e^{e^2}}{2}$
12) $x = 28$
13) $x = 80$
14) 0
15) 3
16) 2

17) 2
18) 4
19) -1
20) 10
21) 8
22) 32
23) $\frac{1}{2}$
24) $\frac{9}{25} = 0.36$

25) e

26) 6

27) -2

28) 16

29) $\frac{2}{e}$

30) 0

31) 3

32) -0.5

33) $4e^{-2} = \frac{4}{e^2}$

34) $\frac{1}{e}$

35) $3e$

Solving Logarithmic Equations

1) $\{-\frac{1}{2}\}$

2) $\{\frac{1}{175}\}$

3) $\{-\frac{1}{1,000}\}$

4) $\{4,000\}$

5) $\{5,000\}$

6) $\{1\}$

7) $\{6\}$

8) $\{83\}$

9) $\{1\}$

10) $\{2\}$

11) $\{\frac{7}{9}\}$

12) $\{-2\}$

13) No Solution

14) No Solution

15) $\{8, -2\}$

16) $\{6\}$

17) $\{\sqrt{3}, -\sqrt{3}\}$

18) $\{\frac{1}{28}\}$

19) $x = \frac{2-2e}{3e} = -0.42$

20) $\{\frac{11}{2}\}$

21) $e^3 - 1$

22) $\{8\}$

23) $\{2\}$

24) $\{6.23\}$

25) $x = \frac{e^5 - 2}{4}$

26) $x = 4 + \sqrt{3}$

27) $x = \frac{e^4 - 4}{6}$

28) No Solution

29) $\{1\}$

30) No Solution

31) $x > 3$

32) $\{2, 4\}$

33) $\{0.71667 \dots\}$

34) $\{\frac{17}{6}\}$

35) $\{-1\}$

36) $\{3\}$

Chapter 18: Circles

Math Topics that you'll learn in this Chapter:

- ✓ Circumference and Area of Circles
- ✓ Arc length and sector Area
- ✓ Equation of a Circle
- ✓ Finding the Center and the Radius of Circles

155

Circumference and Area of circle

✍ **Find the Circumference of each circle.** (π = 3.14)

1) _____   2) _____   3) _____   4) _____   5) _____   6) _____

 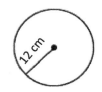 

7) _____   8) _____   9) _____   10) _____   11) _____   12) _____

✍ **Complete the table below.** (π = 3.14)

	Radius	Diameter	Circumference	Area
Circle 1	2 inches	4 inches	12.56 inches	12.56 square inches
Circle 2		8 meters		
Circle 3				113.04 square ft
Circle 4			50.24 miles	
Circle 5		9 km		
Circle 6	7 cm			
Circle 7		10 feet		
Circle 8				615.44 square meters
Circle 9			81.64 inches	
Circle 10	12 feet			

bit.ly/3nWFuRC

Find more at

EffortlessMath.com

Arc Length and Sector Area

✑ *Find the length of each arc. Round your answers to the nearest hundredth.*

1) $r = 4\ cm, \theta = 28° \rightarrow arc =$ ___

6) $r = 3\ in, \theta = 20° \rightarrow arc =$ ___

2) $r = 6\ ft, \theta = 30° \rightarrow arc =$ ___

7) $r = 7\ cm, \theta = 66° \rightarrow arc =$ ___

3) $r = 8\ ft, \theta = 40° \rightarrow arc =$ ___

8) $r = 6\ ft, \theta = 80° \rightarrow arc =$ ___

4) $r = 12\ cm, \theta = 34° \rightarrow arc =$ ___

9) $r = 11\ ft, \theta = 68° \rightarrow arc =$ ___

5) $r = 10\ in, \theta = 70° \rightarrow arc =$ ___

10) $r = 5\ in, \theta = 42° \rightarrow arc =$ ___

✑ *Find area of each sector. Round your answers to the nearest tenth.*

11)

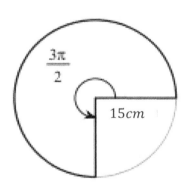

Area of the sector: _____

12)

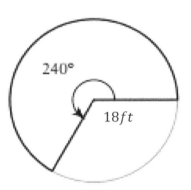

Area of the sector: _____

Equation of a Circle

✎ **Write the standard form equation of each circle.**

1) $x^2 + y^2 - 4x + 2y - 4 = 0 \rightarrow$ _____

2) $x^2 + y^2 - 8x + 6y - 11 = 0 \rightarrow$ _____

3) $x^2 + y^2 - 10x - 12y + 12 = 0 \rightarrow$ _____

4) $x^2 + y^2 + 12x - 6y - 19 = 0 \rightarrow$ _____

5) $x^2 + y^2 - 6x + 8y + 24 = 0 \rightarrow$ _____

6) $x^2 + y^2 - 14x - 8y - 16 = 0 \rightarrow$ _____

7) $x^2 + y^2 + 10x + 2y - 10 = 0 \rightarrow$ _____

8) $x^2 + y^2 - 4x + 10y - 7 = 0 \rightarrow$ _____

9) $x^2 + y^2 + 8x - 2y - 8 = 0 \rightarrow$ _____

10) $x^2 + y^2 + 4x - 4y - 1 = 0 \rightarrow$ _____

11) *Center:*$(-6, 5)$*, Radius:* $4 \rightarrow$ _____

12) *Center:*$(7, -3)$*, Radius:* $3 \rightarrow$ _____

13) *Center:*$(-6, 5)$*, Area:* $25\pi \rightarrow$ _____

14) *Center:*$(-6, 2)$*, Area:* $49\pi \rightarrow$ _____

15) *Center:*$(-1, -5)$*, Circumference:* $2\sqrt{3}\pi \rightarrow$ _____

Finding the Center and the Radius of Circles

✎ *Identify the center and radius of each.*

1) $(x + 1)^2 + (y - 2)^2 = 5 \rightarrow$ *Center:* (__ , __)*, Radius:* ____

2) $(x - 5)^2 + (y + 10)^2 = 4 \rightarrow$ *Center:* (__ , __)*, Radius:* ____

3) $x^2 + (y - 3)^2 = 8 \rightarrow$ *Center:* (__ , __)*, Radius:* ____

4) $(x - 1)^2 + y^2 = 9 \rightarrow$ *Center:* (__ , __)*, Radius:* ____

5) $x^2 + y^2 = 16 \rightarrow$ *Center:* (__ , __)*, Radius:* ____

6) $(x + 1)^2 + (y + 6)^2 = 10 \rightarrow$ *Center:* (__ , __)*, Radius:* ____

7) $x^2 + y^2 + 4x + 4 = 9 \rightarrow$ *Center:* (__ , __)*, Radius:* ____

8) $x^2 + y^2 + 10x = 4y - 4 \rightarrow$ *Center:* (__ , __)*, Radius:* ____

9) $x^2 + y^2 + 8x + 2y = -1 \rightarrow$ *Center:* (__ , __)*, Radius:* ____

10) $x^2 + y^2 - 2x - 2y - 7 = 0 \rightarrow$ *Center:* (__ , __)*, Radius:* ____

11) $x^2 + y^2 + 6x = 6y - 9 \rightarrow$ *Center:* (__ , __)*, Radius:* ____

12) $x^2 + y^2 + 12x = 2y - 1 \rightarrow$ *Center:* (__ , __)*, Radius:* ____

Answers – Chapter 18

Circumference and Area of circle

1) $43.96\ in$
2) $75.36\ cm$
3) $87.92\ ft$
4) $81.64\ m$

5) $113.04\ cm$
6) $94.2\ miles$
7) $119.32\ in$
8) $138.16\ ft$

9) $157\ m$
10) $175.84\ m$
11) $219.8\ in$
12) $314\ ft$

	Radius	Diameter	Circumference	Area
Circle 1	2 inches	4 inches	12.56 inches	12.56 square inches
Circle 2	4 meters	8 meters	25.12 meters	50.24 square meters
Circle 3	6 ft	12 ft	37.68	113.04 square ft
Circle 4	8 miles	16 miles	50.24 miles	200.96 square miles
Circle 5	4.5 km	9 km	28.26 km	63.585 square km
Circle 6	7 cm	14 cm	43.96 cm	153.86 square cm
Circle 7	5 feet	10 feet	31.4 feet	78.5 square feet
Circle 8	14 m	28 m	87.92 m	615.44 square meters
Circle 9	13 in	26 in	81.64 inches	530.66 square inches
Circle 10	12 feet	24 feet	75.36 feet	452.16 square feet

Arc Length and Sector Area

1) $1.95\ cm$
2) $3.14\ ft$
3) $5.58\ ft$
4) $7.12\ cm$

5) $12.21\ in$
6) $10.05\ in$
7) $8.06\ cm$
8) $8.37\ ft$

9) $13.05\ ft$
10) $3.66\ in$
11) $529.9\ cm^2$
12) $678.2\ ft^2$

Equation of a Circle

1) $(x-2)^2 + \left(y-(-1)\right)^2 = 3^2$
2) $(x-4)^2 + \left(y-(-3)\right)^2 = 6^2$
3) $(x-5)^2 + (y-6)^2 = 7^2$
4) $\left(x-(-6)\right)^2 + (y-3)^2 = 8^2$
5) $(x-3)^2 + \left(y-(-4)\right)^2 = 1^2$
6) $(x-7)^2 + (y-4)^2 = 9^2$
7) $\left(x-(-5)\right)^2 + \left(y-(-1)\right)^2 = 6^2$
8) $(x-2)^2 + \left(y-(-5)\right)^2 = 6^2$

9) $\left(x-(-4)\right)^2 + (y-1)^2 = 5^2$
10) $\left(x-(-2)\right)^2 + (y-2)^2 = 3^2$
11) $\left(x-(-6)\right)^2 + (y-5)^2 = 4^2$
12) $(x-7)^2 + \left(y-(-3)\right)^2 = 3^2$
13) $\left(x-(-6)\right)^2 + (y-5)^2 = 5^2$
14) $\left(x-(-6)\right)^2 + (y-2)^2 = 7^2$
15) $(x-(-1))^2 + (y-(-5))^2 = 3$

Finding the Center and the Radius of Circles

1) Center: $(-1, 2)$, Radius: $\sqrt{5}$

2) Center: $(5, -10)$, Radius: 2

3) Center: $(0, 3)$, Radius: $2\sqrt{2}$

4) Center: $(1, 0)$, Radius: 3

5) Center: $(0, 0)$, Radius: 4

6) Center: $(-1, -6)$, Radius: $\sqrt{10}$

7) Center: $(-2, 0)$, Radius: 3

8) Center: $(-5, 2)$, Radius: 5

9) Center: $(-4, -1)$, Radius: 4

10) Center: $(1, 1)$, Radius: 3

11) Center: $(-3, 3)$, Radius: 3

12) Center: $(-6, 1)$, Radius: 6

Chapter 19: Rational Expressions

Math Topics that you'll learn in this Chapter:

- ✓ Simplifying Complex Fractions
- ✓ Graphing Rational Expressions
- ✓ Adding and Subtracting Rational Expressions
- ✓ Multiplying Rational Expressions
- ✓ Dividing Rational Expressions
- ✓ Rational Equations

Simplifying Complex Fractions

✎**Simplify each expression.**

1) $\dfrac{\frac{2}{5}}{\frac{4}{7}} =$ _____

2) $\dfrac{6}{\frac{5}{x}+\frac{2}{3x}} =$ _____

3) $\dfrac{1-\frac{2}{x-1}}{1+\frac{4}{x+1}} =$ _____

4) $\dfrac{x}{\frac{3}{4}-\frac{5}{x}} =$ _____

5) $\dfrac{\frac{4}{x-1}}{\frac{5}{x^2+3x-4}} =$ _____

6) $\dfrac{\frac{x+1}{2}}{\frac{x+5}{x-1}} =$ _____

7) $\dfrac{\frac{5}{x}-\frac{4}{x}}{15} =$ _____

8) $\dfrac{\frac{10}{3}}{\frac{9}{4}} =$ _____

9) $\dfrac{10}{\frac{2}{x}+\frac{3}{4x}} =$ _____

10) $\dfrac{x}{\frac{2}{3}-\frac{3}{x}} =$ _____

11) $\dfrac{\frac{x+8}{2}}{\frac{x^2}{2}-\frac{9}{2}} =$ _____

12) $\dfrac{\frac{x-2}{x-5}}{\frac{x-4}{x+9}} =$ _____

13) $\dfrac{\frac{x-2}{x-1}}{\frac{x+1}{x-4}} =$ _____

14) $\dfrac{\frac{1}{x-4}}{\frac{x-5}{2}} =$ _____

15) $\dfrac{1+\frac{3}{x+2}}{1-\frac{5}{x+4}} =$ _____

16) $\dfrac{\frac{2}{x+3}}{\frac{6}{x^2+5x+6}} =$ _____

Graphing Rational Expressions

 **Graph rational expressions.**

1) $f(x) = \dfrac{x^2}{5x+6}$

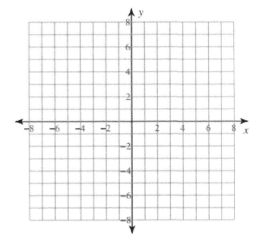

2) $f(x) = \dfrac{x^2+8x+10}{x+5}$

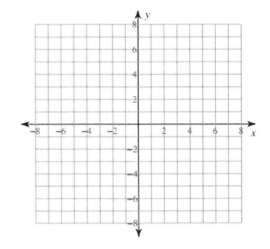

3) $f(x) = \dfrac{2x-4}{3x^2+6x+1}$

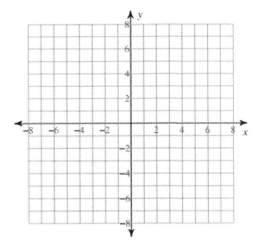

4) $f(x) = \dfrac{x^2+6x}{x+4}$

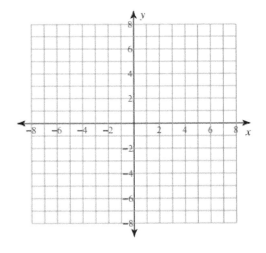

bit.ly/2PmZol8

Find more at

Adding and Subtracting Rational Expressions

✎ **Simplify each expression**.

1) $\dfrac{5}{x+2} + \dfrac{x-1}{x+2} = $ _____

2) $\dfrac{6}{x+5} - \dfrac{5}{x+5} = $ _____

3) $\dfrac{7}{4x+10} + \dfrac{x-5}{4x+10} = $ _____

4) $\dfrac{9x}{x+2} + \dfrac{x-1}{x+3} = $ _____

5) $\dfrac{9}{x+7} + \dfrac{x+1}{x+3} = $ _____

6) $\dfrac{x+3}{5x+2} + \dfrac{x+8}{5x+2} = $ _____

7) $\dfrac{4}{3x+2} - \dfrac{2}{x+4} = $ _____

8) $\dfrac{x+8}{x+6} + \dfrac{x-8}{x+6} = $ _____

9) $\dfrac{8}{x^2-5x+4} + \dfrac{2}{x^2-16} = $ _____

10) $\dfrac{15}{x^2-6x+5} - \dfrac{4}{x-5} = $ _____

11) $\dfrac{5}{6x-2} + \dfrac{x}{6x-2} = $ _____

12) $\dfrac{x+2}{x+3} + \dfrac{4}{x+1} = $ _____

13) $\dfrac{8}{x+3} - \dfrac{5}{x+1} = $ _____

14) $\dfrac{8x}{4x+5} - \dfrac{6x}{2x+3} = $ _____

15) $\dfrac{3x}{2x+3} - \dfrac{x}{3x+2} = $ _____

16) $\dfrac{x+6}{4x+1} - \dfrac{x-6}{4x+1} = $ _____

17) $\dfrac{9}{x+5} + \dfrac{6}{x+4} = $ _____

18) $\dfrac{6}{x+4} - \dfrac{2}{x^2-16} = $ _____

19) $\dfrac{x-4}{x^2-4} + \dfrac{x+1}{4-x^2} = $ _____

20) $\dfrac{12}{x^2-49} - \dfrac{5}{x+7} = $ _____

Multiplying Rational Expressions

✎ *Simplify each expression.*

1) $\frac{x+1}{x+5} \times \frac{x+6}{x+1} =$ _____

2) $\frac{x+4}{x+9} \times \frac{x+9}{x+3} =$ _____

3) $\frac{x+8}{x} \times \frac{2}{x+8} =$ _____

4) $\frac{x+5}{x+1} \times \frac{x^2}{x+5} =$ _____

5) $\frac{x-3}{x+2} \times \frac{2x+4}{x+4} =$ _____

6) $\frac{x-6}{x+3} \times \frac{2x+6}{2x} =$ _____

7) $\frac{x+1}{x+5} \times \frac{5x+25}{x^2} =$ _____

8) $\frac{x+7}{x+4} \times \frac{4x+8}{x+7} =$ _____

9) $\frac{80x}{15} \times \frac{9}{10x^2} =$ _____

10) $\frac{44}{12x} \times \frac{24x}{11} =$ _____

11) $\frac{23x}{33} \times \frac{11x^2}{2} =$ _____

12) $\frac{15x^2}{20} \times \frac{12y}{3x^2} =$ _____

13) $\frac{x+9}{2x} \times \frac{4}{3x+27} =$ _____

14) $\frac{18x^2}{32} \times \frac{16}{6x} =$ _____

15) $\frac{x-6}{x+4} \times \frac{x+4}{10x-60} =$ _____

16) $\frac{4x+40}{x+10} \times \frac{x+3}{4} =$ _____

17) $\frac{1}{x+10} \times \frac{10x+60}{x+6} =$ _____

18) $\frac{x+8}{x} \times \frac{5x}{2x+16} =$ _____

19) $\frac{3x}{44} \times \frac{45x^3}{12} =$ _____

20) $\frac{x-7}{x+5} \times \frac{4x+20}{x-7} =$ _____

Dividing Rational Expressions

✏ *Simplify each expression.*

1) $\dfrac{5x}{4} \div \dfrac{5}{2} =$ _____

2) $\dfrac{8}{3x} \div \dfrac{24}{x} =$ _____

3) $\dfrac{3x}{x+4} \div \dfrac{x}{3x+12} =$ _____

4) $\dfrac{2}{5x} \div \dfrac{16}{10x} =$ _____

5) $\dfrac{36x}{5} \div \dfrac{4}{3} =$ _____

6) $\dfrac{15x^2}{6} \div \dfrac{5x}{14} =$ _____

7) $\dfrac{x-3}{x+2} \div \dfrac{x}{x+2} =$ _____

8) $\dfrac{4x}{x-8} \div \dfrac{4x}{x-2} =$ _____

9) $\dfrac{x+2}{5x^2+10x} \div \dfrac{6}{5x} =$ _____

10) $\dfrac{12x}{x-6} \div \dfrac{6}{4x-24} =$ _____

11) $\dfrac{x+4}{x+6} \div \dfrac{x^2+2x-8}{3} =$ _____

12) $\dfrac{x^2+5x+6}{x+1} \div \dfrac{x+2}{x-6} =$

13) $\dfrac{4x+16}{x+2} \div \dfrac{x^2+16x}{x+2} =$ _____

14) $\dfrac{8}{x-4} \div \dfrac{2x}{x^2-x-12} =$ _____

15) $\dfrac{7x+1}{2} \div \dfrac{70x+10}{5} =$ _____

16) $\dfrac{2x+1}{x+4} \div \dfrac{4x^2+2x}{2x+8} =$ _____

17) $\dfrac{3x-2}{x-2} \div \dfrac{9x-6}{x^2-4} =$ _____

18) $\dfrac{25x^3}{9} \div \dfrac{5x^2}{3} =$ _____

19) $\dfrac{x^2+11x+30}{x+10} \div \dfrac{x^2+3x-10}{x^2-100} =$ __

20) $\dfrac{35x^2}{x^2-49} \div \dfrac{5x}{4x-28} =$ __

21) $\dfrac{3x}{2} \div \dfrac{6x}{x+5} =$ _____

22) $\dfrac{2x^4}{x+6} \div \dfrac{3x^2}{x^2-36} =$ _____

Rational Equations

✏️ *Solve each equation.*

1) $\frac{1}{8x^2} = \frac{1}{4x^2} - \frac{1}{x} \rightarrow x = $ _____

2) $\frac{1}{9x^2} + \frac{1}{9x} = \frac{1}{x^2} \rightarrow x = $ _____

3) $\frac{32}{2x^2} + 1 = \frac{8}{x} \rightarrow x = $ _____

4) $\frac{1}{x-5} = \frac{4}{x-5} + 1 \rightarrow x = $ _____

5) $\frac{1}{x^2} + \frac{1}{x} = \frac{1}{4x^2} \rightarrow x = $ _____

6) $\frac{1}{10x^2} = \frac{1}{2x} + \frac{11}{10x^2} \rightarrow x = $ _____

7) $\frac{1}{x^2-x} + \frac{1}{x} = \frac{10}{x^2-x} \rightarrow x = $ _____

8) $\frac{x-5}{6x} = \frac{1}{5x} + 1 \rightarrow x = $ _____

9) $\frac{x-1}{x} + \frac{1}{x^2+2x} = 1 \rightarrow x = $ _____

10) $\frac{x-2}{x+3} - 1 = \frac{3}{x+2} \rightarrow x = $ _____

11) $\frac{x}{10} = \frac{6}{x-4} \rightarrow x = $ _____

12) $\frac{2}{x-2} = \frac{5}{x-1} \rightarrow x = $ _____

13) $\frac{3}{5x} = \frac{5}{9x-2} \rightarrow x = $ _____

14) $\frac{2}{2x-3} = \frac{10}{6x+1} \rightarrow x = $ _____

15) $\frac{2}{x+2} + \frac{3}{x} = \frac{x}{x+2} \rightarrow x = $ _____

16) $\frac{3}{x+1} = \frac{2}{x-3} \rightarrow x = $ _____

17) $\frac{x}{x-2} + \frac{1}{5} = \frac{x+1}{x-2} \rightarrow x = $ _____

18) $\frac{1}{x-4} + \frac{x}{x-2} = \frac{2}{x^2-6x+8} \rightarrow x = $

_____

19) $\frac{x}{x+3} = \frac{8}{x+6} \rightarrow x = $ _____

20) $\frac{x}{x-1} - \frac{2}{x} = \frac{1}{x-1} \rightarrow x = $ _____

Answers – Chapter 19

Simplifying Complex Fractions

1) $\dfrac{7}{10}$

2) $\dfrac{18x}{17}$

3) $\dfrac{x^2-2x-3}{x^2+4x-5}$

4) $\dfrac{4x^2}{3x-20}$

5) $\dfrac{4x+16}{5}$

6) $\dfrac{x^2-1}{2x+10}$

7) $\dfrac{1}{15x}$

8) $\dfrac{40}{27}$

9) $\dfrac{40x}{11}$

10) $\dfrac{3x^2}{2x-9}$

11) $\dfrac{x+8}{x^2-9}$

12) $\dfrac{x^2+7x-18}{x^2-9x+20}$

13) $\dfrac{x^2-6x+8}{x^2-1}$

14) $\dfrac{2}{x^2-9x+20}$

15) $\dfrac{x^2+9x+20}{x^2+x-2}$

16) $\dfrac{x+2}{3}$

Graphing Rational Expressions

1) $f(x) = \dfrac{x^2}{5x+6}$

2) $f(x) = \dfrac{x^2+8x+10}{x+5}$

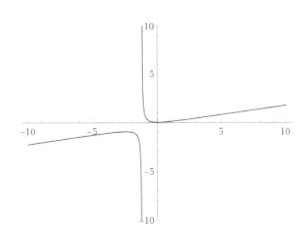

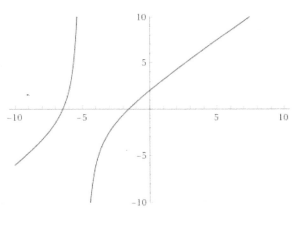

3) $f(x) = \dfrac{2x-4}{3x^2+6x+1}$ 4) $f(x) = \dfrac{x^2+6x}{x+4}$

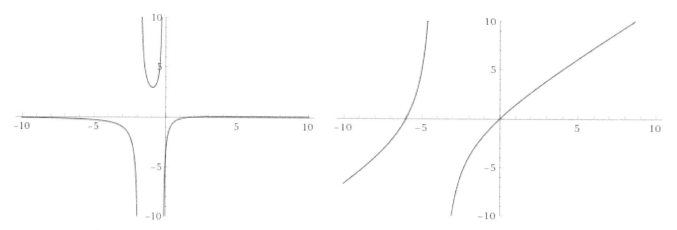

Adding and Subtracting Rational Expressions

1) $\dfrac{x+4}{x+2}$

2) $\dfrac{1}{x+5}$

3) $\dfrac{x+2}{4x+10}$

4) $\dfrac{10x^2+28x-2}{(x+2)(x+3)}$

5) $\dfrac{x^2+17x+34}{(x+7)(x+3)}$

6) $\dfrac{2x+11}{5x+2}$

7) $\dfrac{-2x+12}{(3x+2)(x+4)}$

8) $\dfrac{2x}{x+6}$

9) $\dfrac{10x+30}{(x-4)(x+4)(x-1)}$

10) $\dfrac{-4x+19}{(x-1)(x-5)}$

11) $\dfrac{x+5}{6x-2}$

12) $\dfrac{x^2+7x+14}{(x+3)(x+1)}$

13) $\dfrac{3x-7}{(x+3)(x+1)}$

14) $\dfrac{-8x^2-6x}{(4x+5)(2x+3)}$

15) $\dfrac{7x^2+3x}{(2x+3)(3x+2)}$

16) $\dfrac{12}{4x+1}$

17) $\dfrac{15x+66}{(x+5)(x+4)}$

18) $\dfrac{6x-26}{(x+4)(x-4)}$

19) $-\dfrac{5}{(x-2)(x+2)}$

20) $\dfrac{-5x+47}{(x+7)(x-7)}$

Multiplying Rational Expressions

1) $\dfrac{x+6}{x+5}$

2) $\dfrac{x+4}{x+3}$

3) $\dfrac{2}{x}$

4) $\dfrac{x^2}{x+1}$

5) $\dfrac{2(x-3)}{x+4}$

6) $\dfrac{x-6}{x}$

7) $\dfrac{5(x+1)}{x^2}$

8) 2

9) $\dfrac{24}{5x}$

10) 8

11) $\dfrac{23x^3}{6}$

12) $3y$

13) $\dfrac{2}{3x}$

14) $\dfrac{3x}{2}$

15) $\dfrac{1}{10}$

16) $x+3$

17) $\dfrac{10}{x+10}$

18) $\dfrac{5}{2}$

19) $\dfrac{45x^4}{176}$

20) $\dfrac{4(x-2)}{x-7}$

Effortless

Math

Education

Dividing Rational Expressions

1) $\dfrac{x}{2}$

2) $\dfrac{1}{9}$

3) 9

4) $\dfrac{1}{4}$

5) $\dfrac{27}{5}$

6) 7

7) $\dfrac{x-3}{x}$

8) $\dfrac{x-2}{x-8}$

9) $\dfrac{1}{6}$

10) $8x$

11) $\dfrac{3}{(x+6)(x-2)}$

12) $\dfrac{(x+3)(x-6)}{x+1}$

13) $\dfrac{4(x+4)}{x^2+16x}$

14) $\dfrac{4(x+3)}{x}$

15) $\dfrac{1}{4}$

16) $\dfrac{1}{x}$

17) $\dfrac{x+2}{3}$

18) $\dfrac{5}{3}$

19) $\dfrac{(x+6)(x-10)}{x-2}$

20) $\dfrac{28x}{x+7}$

21) $\dfrac{x+5}{4}$

22) $\dfrac{2x^2(x-6)}{3}$

Rational Equations

1) $x = \dfrac{1}{8}$

2) $x = 8$

3) $x = 4$

4) $x = 2$

5) $x = -\dfrac{3}{4}$

6) $x = -2$

7) $x = 10$

8) $x = -\dfrac{31}{25}$

9) $x = -1$

10) $x = -\dfrac{19}{8}$

11) $x = 10, x = -6$

12) $x = \dfrac{8}{3}$

13) $x = 3$

14) $x = 4$

15) $x = 6, x = -1$

16) $x = 11$

17) $x = 7$

18) $x = -1$

19) $x = 6, x = -4$

20) $x = 2$

Chapter 20:
Trigonometric
Functions

Math Topics that you'll learn in this Chapter:

- ✓ Evaluating Each Trigonometric Function
- ✓ Trig ratios of General Angles
- ✓ Angle and Angle Measure
- ✓ Finding Co–Terminal Angles and Reference Angles
- ✓ Missing Sides and Angles of a Right Triangle

175

Evaluating Trigonometric Functions

✍ *Find the exact value of each trigonometric function.*

1) $\cos 225° =$ _____

2) $\tan \dfrac{7\pi}{6} =$ _____

3) $\tan -\dfrac{\pi}{6} =$ _____

4) $\cot -\dfrac{7\pi}{6} =$ _____

5) $\cos -\dfrac{\pi}{4} =$ _____

6) $\cos -480° =$ _____

7) $\sin 690° =$ _____

8) $\tan 420° =$ _____

9) $\cot - 495° =$ _____

10) $\tan 405° =$ _____

11) $\cot 390° =$ _____

12) $\cos - 300° =$ _____

13) $\cot - 210° =$ _____

✍ *Use the given point on the terminal side of angle θ to find the value of the trigonometric function indicated.*

14) $\sin\theta, \ (-6, 4)$

15) $\cos\theta, \ (2, -2)$

16) $\cot\theta, \ (-7, \sqrt{15})$

17) $\cos\theta, \ (-5, -12)$

18) $\sin\theta, \ (-\sqrt{7}, 3)$

19) $\tan\theta, \ (-11, -2)$

Trig ratios of General Angles

✎ **Evaluate.**

1) $sin -60° =$ _____

2) $sin 150° =$ _____

3) $cos 315° =$ _____

4) $cos 180° =$ _____

5) $sin 120° =$ _____

6) $sin -330° =$ _____

7) $tan -90° =$ _____

8) $cot 90° =$ _____

9) $tan 270° =$ _____

10) $cot 150° =$ _____

11) $sec 120° =$ _____

12) $csc -360° =$ _____

13) $cot -270° =$ _____

14) $sec 90° =$ _____

15) $cos - 90° =$ _____

16) $sec 60° =$ _____

17) $csc 480° =$ _____

18) $cot -135° =$ _____

✎ **Find the exact value of each trigonometric function. Some may be undefined.**

19) $sec \pi =$ _____

20) $tan -\dfrac{3\pi}{2} =$ _____

21) $cos \dfrac{11\pi}{6} =$ _____

22) $cot \dfrac{5\pi}{3} =$ _____

23) $sec -\dfrac{3\pi}{4} =$ _____

24) $sec \dfrac{\pi}{3} =$ _____

25) $csc \dfrac{5\pi}{6} =$ _____

26) $cot \dfrac{4\pi}{3} =$ _____

27) $csc -\dfrac{3\pi}{4} =$ _____

28) $cot \dfrac{2\pi}{3} =$ _____

bit.ly/3evyQxm

Find more at

Angles and Angle Measure

✎ **Convert each degree measure into radians.**

1) $-140° = $ _____

2) $320° = $ _____

3) $210° = $ _____

4) $780° = $ _____

5) $-190° = $ _____

6) $345° = $ _____

7) $-150° = $ _____

8) $420° = $ _____

9) $300° = $ _____

10) $-60° = $ _____

11) $315° = $ _____

12) $600° = $ _____

13) $-720° = $ _____

14) $-160° = $ _____

15) $-210° = $ _____

16) $960° = $ _____

17) $-30° = $ _____

18) $660° = $ _____

19) $-240° = $ _____

20) $840° = $ _____

21) $1,200° = $ _____

✎ **Convert each radian measure into degrees.**

22) $\dfrac{\pi}{30} = $

23) $\dfrac{4\pi}{5} = $

24) $\dfrac{7\pi}{18} = $

25) $\dfrac{\pi}{5} = $

26) $-\dfrac{5\pi}{4} = $

27) $\dfrac{14\pi}{3} = $

28) $-\dfrac{16\pi}{3} = $

29) $-\dfrac{3\pi}{5} = $

30) $\dfrac{11\pi}{6} = $

31) $\dfrac{5\pi}{9} = $

32) $-\dfrac{\pi}{3} = $

33) $\dfrac{13\pi}{6} = $

34) $\dfrac{9\pi}{4} = $

35) $\dfrac{21\pi}{4} = $

36) $-\dfrac{4\pi}{15} = $

37) $\dfrac{14\pi}{3} = $

38) $-\dfrac{41\pi}{12} = $

39) $-\dfrac{17\pi}{9} = $

Finding Co-terminal Angles and Reference Angles

✎ *Find a conterminal angle between 0° and 360° for each angle provided.*

1) $-440° =$

2) $640° =$

3) $-435° =$

4) $-330° =$

✎ *Find a conterminal angle between 0 and 2π for each given angle.*

5) $\dfrac{15\pi}{4} =$

6) $-\dfrac{19\pi}{12} =$

7) $-\dfrac{35\pi}{18} =$

8) $\dfrac{11\pi}{3} =$

✎ *Find the reference angle of each angle.*

9)

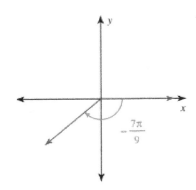

$-\dfrac{7\pi}{9}$

10)

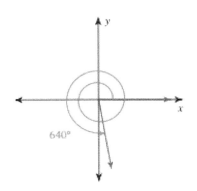

$640°$

Missing Sides and Angles of a Right Triangle

✎ *Find the value of each trigonometric ratio as fractions in their simplest form.*

1) $\tan A$

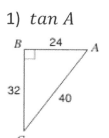

2) $\sin x$

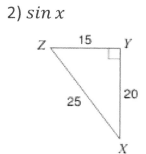

✎ *Find the missing sides. Round answers to the nearest tenth.*

3)

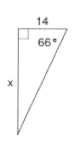

4)

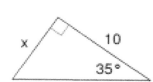

5)

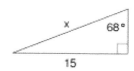

6)

Answers – Chapter 20

Evaluating Each Trigonometric Function

1) $-\frac{\sqrt{2}}{2}$

2) $\frac{\sqrt{3}}{3}$

3) $-\frac{\sqrt{3}}{3}$

4) $-\sqrt{3}$

5) $\frac{\sqrt{2}}{2}$

6) $-\frac{1}{2}$

7) $-\frac{1}{2}$

8) $\sqrt{3}$

9) 1

10) 1

11) $\sqrt{3}$

12) $\frac{1}{2}$

13) $-\sqrt{3}$

14) $\frac{2\sqrt{13}}{13}$

15) $\sqrt{2}$

16) $-\frac{7\sqrt{15}}{15}$

17) $-\frac{5}{13}$

18) $\frac{3}{4}$

19) $\frac{2}{11}$

Trig Ratios of General Angles

1) $-\frac{\sqrt{3}}{2}$

2) $\frac{1}{2}$

3) $\frac{\sqrt{2}}{2}$

4) -1

5) $\frac{\sqrt{3}}{2}$

6) $\frac{1}{2}$

7) Undefined

8) 0

9) Undefined

10) $-\sqrt{3}$

11) -2

12) 1

13) 0

14) Undefined

15) 0

16) 2

17) $\frac{2\sqrt{3}}{3}$

18) 1

19) -1

20) Undefined

21) $\frac{\sqrt{3}}{2}$

22) $-\frac{\sqrt{3}}{3}$

23) $-\sqrt{2}$

24) 2

25) 2

26) $\frac{\sqrt{3}}{3}$

27) $-\sqrt{2}$

28) $-\frac{\sqrt{3}}{3}$

Angles and Angle Measure

1) $-\frac{7\pi}{9}$

2) $\frac{16\pi}{9}$

3) $\frac{7\pi}{6}$

4) $\frac{13\pi}{3}$

5) $-\frac{19\pi}{18}$

6) $\frac{23\pi}{12}$

7) $-\frac{5\pi}{6}$

8) $\frac{7\pi}{3}$

9) $\frac{5\pi}{3}$

10) $-\frac{\pi}{3}$

11) $\frac{7\pi}{4}$

12) $\frac{10\pi}{3}$

13) -4π

14) $-\frac{8\pi}{9}$

Effortless Math Education

15) $-\frac{7\pi}{6}$

16) $\frac{16\pi}{3}$

17) $-\frac{\pi}{6}$

18) $\frac{11\pi}{3}$

19) $-\frac{4\pi}{3}$

20) $\frac{14\pi}{3}$

21) $\frac{20\pi}{3}$

22) $6°$

23) $144°$

24) $70°$

25) $36°$

Finding Co−Terminal Angles and Reference Angles

1) $280°$

2) $280°$

3) $285°$

4) $30°$

5) $\frac{7\pi}{4}$

6) $\frac{5\pi}{12}$

7) $\frac{\pi}{18}$

8) $\frac{5\pi}{3}$

9) $\frac{2\pi}{9}$

10) $80°$

Missing Sides and Angles of a Right Triangle

1) $\frac{4}{3}$

2) $\frac{3}{5}$

3) 31.4

4) 7.0

5) 16.2

6) 31.1

Time to Test

Time to refine your skill with a practice examination

In this section, there are 2 complete ALEKS Mathematics Tests. Take these tests to simulate the test day experience. After you've finished, score your test using the answers and explanations section.

Before You Start

- You'll need a pencil and scratch papers to take the test.

- For these practice tests, don't time yourself. Spend time as much as you need.

- After you've finished the test, review the answer key to see where you went wrong.

Good Luck!

ALEKS Mathematics

Practice Test 1

2023

Total number of questions: 35

Total time: No time limit

Calculators are permitted for ALEKS Math Test.

185

1) A line passes through the point (9,5) and has a slope of $\frac{2}{3}$.

   Write an equation in point-slope form for this line.

2) Evaluate.

   $(-8)^3 =$

   $-5^4 =$

3) Point A lies on the line with equation $y - 3 = 2(x + 5)$. If the x-coordinate of A is 8, what is the y-coordinate of A?

4) In the following table, for each ordered pair (x, y), determine whether it is solution to the inequality $y < 5x^2 - 2x - 5$.

(x, y)	Is it a solution?	
	Yes	No
$(-2, 8)$		
$(3, 6)$		
$(1, 12)$		
$(-1, 6)$		

5) Factor this polynomial completely.

   $5v^3 - 3v^2 + 20v - 12$

6) What is the ratio of the minimum value to the maximum value of the following function?
$$f(x) = -3x + 1; -2 \leq x \leq 3$$

7) in the tringle below, if the measure of angle A is 37 degrees, then what is the value of y? (figure is NOT drawn to scale)

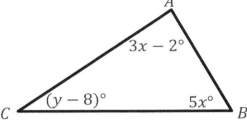

8) If the following equations are true, what is the value of x?
$$a = \sqrt{3}$$
$$4a = \sqrt{4x}$$

9) If $\sqrt{4m - 3} = m$, what is (are) the value(s) of m?

10) Multiply and write the product in scientific notation:
$$(2.9 \times 10^6) \times (2.6 \times 10^{-5})$$

11) If $x \neq -4$ and $x \neq 5$, simplify $\dfrac{1}{\frac{1}{x-5}+\frac{1}{x+4}}$.

12) Calculate $f(5)$ for the following function f.
$$f(x) = x^2 - 3x$$

13) In the following figure, ABCD is a rectangle, and E and F are points on AD and DC, respectively. The area of $\triangle BED$ is 16, and the area of $\triangle BDF$ is 18. What is the perimeter of the rectangle?

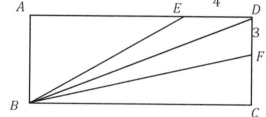

14) Solve for x: $\dfrac{2x}{x-3} = \dfrac{2x+2}{2x-6}$

15) A ladder leans against a wall forming a 60° angle between the ground and the ladder. If the bottom of the ladder is 30 feet away from the wall, how long is the ladder?

16) Convert radian measure $\frac{2\pi}{3}$ to degree measure.

17) Find positive and negative Coterminal angles to angle $\frac{\pi}{2}$.

18) In the following figure, ABCD is a rectangle. If $a = \sqrt{3}$, and $b = 2a$, find the area of the shaded region. (the shaded region is a trapezoid)

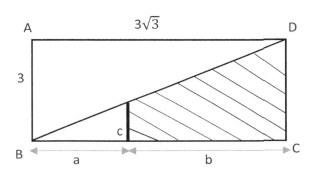

19) Find the equation of a circle in the xy-plane with center $(-1, 2)$ and a radius with endpoint $(2, 6)$.

20) A construction company is building a wall. The company can build 30 cm of the wall per minute. After 40 minutes $\frac{3}{4}$ of the wall is completed. How many meters is the wall?

21) Find side AC in the following triangle. Round your answer to the nearest tenth.

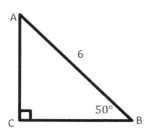

22) The perimeter of a rectangular yard is 72 meters. What is its length if its width is twice its length?

23) If the ratio of $5a$ to $2b$ is $\frac{1}{10}$, what is the ratio of a to b?

24) If θ is an acute angle and $sin\ \theta = \frac{4}{5}$ then $cos\ \theta = ?$

25) If 60% of x equal to 30% of 20, then what is the value of $(x + 5)^2$?

26) A boat sails 40 miles south and then 30 miles east. How far is the boat from its start point?

27) What is the value of x in the following equation? $log_4(x + 2) - log_4(x - 2) = 1$

28) If $f(x) = x + 6$ and $g(x) = -x^2 - 2x - 1$, then find $(g - f)(x)$.

29) What is the area of the following equilateral triangle if the side $AB = 8\ cm$?

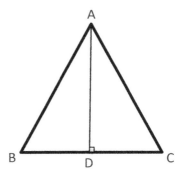

30) If $y = 4ab + 3b^3$, what is y when $a = 2$ and $b = 3$?

31) Simplify. $\frac{(4u^{-5}v^3)^{-2}}{6w}$

Write the expression with positive powers.

32) Solve for x: $3 + \frac{2x}{x-7} = \frac{5}{7-x}$

33) Simplify the inequality $|16 - 8x| < 32$

34) Simplify and express in the form $a + bi$: $\frac{-8i}{12+i}$

35) Sketch the graph of $2y > 4x^2$

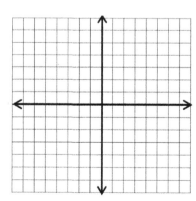

This is the end of Practice Test 1

ALEKS Mathematics

Practice Test 2

2023

Total number of questions: 35

Total time: No time limit

Calculators are permitted for ALEKS Math Test.

193

1) Factor.

$4x^2 - 49$

2) Solve for x.

$7x^2 - 28x = 0$

3) Two consecutive odd integers have a sum of 28. Find the integers.

4) The equation of a line is given below. $-8x - 2y = 4$
Find the slope and y-intercept.
Then use them to graph the line.
Slope: _____

y-intercept: _____

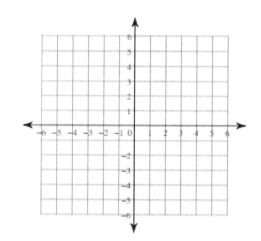

5) Find the domain and range for $f(x) = x^2 + 2$

6) What is the value of y in the following system of equations?
$$2x + 5y = 11$$
$$4x - 2y = -14$$

7) Solve the equation: $log_3(x + 20) - log_3(x + 2) = 1$

8) Write as a single fraction.

$$-4 + \frac{2a - 6y}{12a} - \frac{6a + 4y}{8a}$$

Simplify your answer as much as possible.

9) If $f(x) = 2x^3 + 5x^2 + 2x$ and $g(x) = -3$, what is the value of $f(g(x))$?

10) If the area of a circle is 64 square meters, what is its radius?

11) If one angle of a right triangle measures 60°, what is the sine of the other acute angle?

12) In the figure below, line A is parallel to line B. What is the value of angle x?

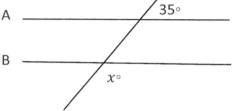

13) An angle is equal to one fifth of its supplement. What is the measure of that angle?

14) Simplify $\frac{4-3i}{-4i}$?

15) The average of five consecutive numbers is 40. What is the smallest number?

16) If $sin\ A = \frac{1}{4}$ in a right triangle and the angle A is an acute angle, then what is $cos\ A$?

17) In the standard (x, y) coordinate system plane, what is the area of the circle with the following equation?

$$(x + 2)^2 + (y - 4)^2 = 16$$

18) What is the slope of a line that is perpendicular to the line

$$4x - 2y = 14?$$

19) If $f(x) = 2x^3 + 4$ and $g(x) = \frac{1}{x}$, what is the value of $f(g(x))$?

20) If 150% of a number is 75, then what is 90% of that number?

21) If cotangent of an angel β is 1, then the tangent of angle β is ...

22) Simplify this expression: $\sqrt{\frac{x^2}{2} + \frac{x^2}{16}}$?

23) If $\tan x = \frac{8}{15}$, then $\sin x =$

$$f(x) = \frac{1}{(x-3)^2 + 4(x-3) + 4}$$

24) For what value of x is the function $f(x)$ above undefinded?

25) What are the zeroes of the function $f(x) = x^3 + 6x^2 + 8x$?

26) Simplify as much as possible: $\frac{5}{x^2} + \frac{7x-3}{x^3}$

27) In the following figure, point Q lies on line n, what is the value of y if $x = 35$?

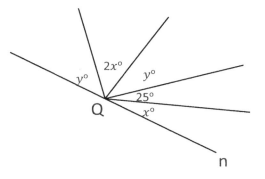

28) Find the answer. $(3n^2 + 4n + 6) - (2n^2 - 5)$

29) The diagonal of a rectangle is 10 inches long and the height of the rectangle is 8 inches. What is the perimeter of the rectangle?

30) Sara opened a bank account that earns 2 percent compounded annually. Her initial deposit was $1,500, and she uses the expression $\$1,500(x)^n$ to find the value of the account after n years. What is the value of x in the expression?

31) Sketch the graph of $y + 3 = 2(x - 1)$.

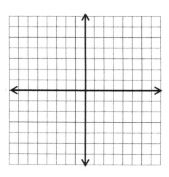

32) Perform the indicated operation and write the result in standard form: $(-7 + 12i)(-5 - 15i)$

33) Write in terms of $log(r), log(s), log(t)$: $log \frac{s\sqrt{t}}{r^2}$

34) What is the least common denominator for $\frac{3x}{x^2-36}$ and $\frac{4}{2x-12}$?

35) Find AC in the following triangle. Round your answer to the nearest tenth.

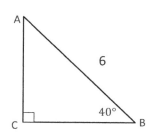

This is the end of Practice Test 2

ALKES Math Practice Tests Answers and Explanations

ALEKS Mathematics Practice Tests Answers and Explanations

Now, it's time to review your results to see where you went wrong and what areas you need to improve!

ALEKS Mathematics Practice Test 1

1) The answer is $y - 5 = \frac{2}{3}(x - 9)$

The "point-slope" form of the equation of a straight line is: $y - y_1 = m(x - x_1)$

The slope of the line is $\frac{2}{3}$ and the point provided is: $(9, 5)$

Then: $y - y_1 = m(x - x_1), m = \frac{2}{3}, (x_1, y_1) = (9, 5) \rightarrow y - 5 = \frac{2}{3}(x - 9)$

The equation in point-slope form of the line is: $y - 5 = \frac{2}{3}(x - 9)$

2) The answers are -512 and -625

$(-8)^3 = (-8)(-8)(-8) = -512$

$-5^4 = -(5)(5)(5)(5) = -625$

3) The answer is 29

Here we can substitute 8 for x in the equation. Thus, $y - 3 = 2(8 + 5), y - 3 = 26$

Adding 3 to both side of the equation: $y = 26 + 3 \rightarrow y = 29$

4) The answer is in the following table

Plug in the values of x and y for each point in the inequality and check the result.

$(-2, 8) \rightarrow y < 5x^2 - 2x - 5 \rightarrow 8 < 5(-2)^2 - 2(-2) - 5 \rightarrow 8 < 19$, this is true!

$(3, 6) \rightarrow y < 5x^2 - 2x - 5 \rightarrow 6 < 5(3)^2 - 2(3) - 5 \rightarrow 6 < 34$, this is true!

$(1, 12) \rightarrow y < 5x^2 - 2x - 5 \rightarrow 12 < 5(1)^2 - 2(1) - 5 \rightarrow 12 < -2$, this is NOT true!

$(-1, 6) \rightarrow y < 5x^2 - 2x - 5 \rightarrow 6 < 5(-1)^2 - 2(-1) - 5 \rightarrow 6 < 2$, this is NOT true!

(x,y)	Is it a solution?	
	Yes	No
$(-2,8)$	Yes	
$(3,6)$	Yes	
$(1,12)$		No
$(-1,6)$		No

5) The answer is $(v^2+4)(5v-3)$

Factor the polynomial by grouping:

$5v^3-3v^2+20v-12=(5v^3-3v^2)+(20v-12)$. Now, factorize each parenthesis. $(5v^3-3v^2)+(20v-12)=v^2(5v-3)+4(5v-3)$. Take the common factor $(5v-3)$ out. Then: $v^2(5v-3)+4(5v-3)=(v^2+4)(5v-3)$

6) The answer is $-\dfrac{8}{7}$

Since $f(x)$ is linear function with a negative slop, then when $x=-2,f(x)$ is maximum and when $x=3,f(x)$ is minimum. Then the ratio of the minimum value to the maximum value of the function is: $\dfrac{f(3)}{f(-2)}=\dfrac{-3(3)+1}{-3(-2)+1}=\dfrac{-8}{7}=-\dfrac{8}{7}$

7) The answer is 86

In the figure angle A is labeled $(3x-2)$ and it measures 37. Thus, $3x-2=37$ and $3x=39$ or $x=13$. That means that angle B, which is labeled $(5x)$, must measure $5\times13=65$. Since the three angles of a triangle must add up to 180,

$37+65+y-8=180$, then: $y+94=108\rightarrow y=180-94=86$

8) The answer is 12

Given the two equations, substitute the numerical value of a into the second equation to solve for x. $a=\sqrt{3},4a=\sqrt{4x}$

Substituting the numerical value for a into the equation with x is as follows.

$4(\sqrt{3}) = \sqrt{4x}$, From here, distribute the 4. $4\sqrt{3} = \sqrt{4x}$

Now square both side of the equation. $(4\sqrt{3})^2 = (\sqrt{4x})^2$

Remember to square both terms within the parentheses. Also, recall that squaring a square root sign cancels them out. $4^2\sqrt{3}^2 = 4x \rightarrow 16(3) = 4x \rightarrow 48 = 4x \rightarrow x = 12$

9) The answer is $m = 1$ and $m = 3$

First square both sides of the equation to get $4m - 3 = m^2$

Subtracting both sides by $4m - 3$ gives us the equation $m^2 - 4m + 3 = 0$

Here you can solve the quadratic equation by factoring to get $(m - 1)(m - 3) = 0$

For the expression $(m - 1)(m - 3)$ to equal zero, $m = 1$ or $m = 3$

10) The answer is 7.54×10

To multiply two numbers in scientific notation, multiply their coefficients and add their exponents. For these two numbers in scientific notation, multiply the coefficients: $2.9 \times 2.6 = 7.54$

Add the powers of 10: $10^6 \times 10^{-5} = 10^{6+(-5)} = 10^1$. Then:

$$(2.9 \times 10^6) \times (2.6 \times 10^{-5}) = (2.9 \times 2.6) \times (10^6 \times 10^{-5}) = 7.54 \times (10^{6+(-5)})$$
$$= 7.54 \times 10^1$$

11) The answer is $\dfrac{(x-5)(x+4)}{(x-5)+(x+4)}$ or $\dfrac{x^2-x-20}{2x-1}$

To rewrite $\dfrac{1}{\frac{1}{x-5}+\frac{1}{x+4}}$, first simplify $\dfrac{1}{x-5} + \dfrac{1}{x+4}$.

$$\frac{1}{x-5} + \frac{1}{x+4} = \frac{1(x+4)}{(x-5)(x+4)} + \frac{1(x-5)}{(x+4)(x-5)} = \frac{(x+4)+(x-5)}{(x+4)(x-5)}$$

Then: $\dfrac{1}{\frac{1}{x-5}+\frac{1}{x+4}} = \dfrac{1}{\frac{(x+4)+(x-5)}{(x+4)(x-5)}} = \dfrac{(x-5)(x+4)}{(x-5)+(x+4)} = \dfrac{x^2-x-20}{2x-1}$. (Remember, $\frac{1}{\frac{1}{x}} = x$)

12) The answer is 10

The input value is 5. Then: $x = 5$. $f(x) = x^2 - 3x \rightarrow f(5) = 5^2 - 3(5) = 25 - 15 = 10$

13) The answer is 40

The area of ΔBED is 16, then: $\frac{4 \times AB}{2} = 16 \rightarrow 4 \times AB = 32 \rightarrow AB = 8$

The area of ΔBDF is 18, then: $\frac{3 \times BC}{2} = 18 \rightarrow 3 \times BC = 36 \rightarrow BC = 12$

The perimeter of the rectangle is = 2 × (width + length) = 2 × (8 + 12) = 40

14) The answer is 1

To solve the equation for x, multiply the numerator and denominator of the rational expression on the left by 2 to get a common denominator $(2x - 6)$. $\frac{2(2x)}{2(x-3)} = \frac{4x}{2x-6}$

Now, the denominators on both side of the equation are equal. Therefore, their numerators must be equal too.

$$\frac{4x}{2x-6} = \frac{2x+2}{2x-6} \rightarrow 4x = 2x + 2 \rightarrow 2x = 2 \rightarrow x = 1$$

15) The answer is 60 ft

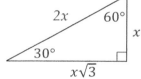

The relationship among all sides of special right triangle

$30° - 60° - 90°$ is provided in this triangle:

In this triangle, the opposite side of 30° angle is half of the hypotenuse.

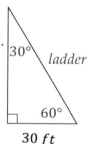

Draw the shape of this question:

The ladder is the hypotenuse. Therefore, the ladder is 60 ft.

16) The answer is 120°

Use this formula: Degrees = Radians $\times \frac{180}{\pi}$

Radians = $\frac{2\pi}{3} \times \frac{180}{\pi} = \frac{360\pi}{3\pi} = 120°$

17) The answers are $-\frac{3\pi}{2}$ and $\frac{5\pi}{2}$

Coterminal angles are equal angles. To find a Coterminal of an angle, add or subtract 360 degrees (or 2π for radians) to the given angle. Then:

Positive angle: $\frac{\pi}{2} + 2\pi = \frac{5\pi}{2}$

Negative angle: $\frac{\pi}{2} - 2\pi = -\frac{3\pi}{2}$

18) The answer is $4\sqrt{3}$

Based on triangle similarity theorem: $\frac{a}{a+b} = \frac{c}{3} \rightarrow c = \frac{3a}{a+b} = \frac{3\sqrt{3}}{3\sqrt{3}} = 1 \rightarrow$ The area of shaded region

is: $\left(\frac{c+3}{2}\right)(b) = \frac{4}{2} \times 2\sqrt{3} = 4\sqrt{3}$

The area of the shaded region is $4\sqrt{3}$ square units.

19) The answer is $(x+1)^2 + (y-2)^2 = 25$

The equation of a circle can be written as $(x-h)^2 + (y-k)^2 = r^2$, where (h, k) is the coordinates of the center of the circle and r is the radius of the circle. Since the coordinates of the center of the circle is $(-1, 2)$, the equation is:

$(x+1)^2 + (y-2)^2 = r^2$, where r is the radius. The radius of the circle is the distance from the center $(-1, 2)$, to the given endpoint of a radius, $(2, 6)$. By the distance formula, $r^2 = (2-(-1))^2 + (6-2)^2 = (3)^2 + (4)^2 = 9 + 16 = 25$

Therefore, an equation of the given circle is $(x+1)^2 + (y-2)^2 = 25$

20) The answer is $16\ meters$

The rate of construction company$= \frac{30\ cm}{1\ min} = 30\ cm/min$

The height of the wall after 40 minutes $= \frac{30\ cm}{1\ min} \times 40\ min = 1,200\ cm$

Let x be the height of wall, then $\frac{3}{4}x = 1,200\ cm \rightarrow x = \frac{4 \times 1,200}{3} \rightarrow x = 1,600\ cm = 16\ meters$

21) The answer is 4. 6

To solve for the side AC, we need to use sine of angle B. Then:
$sin\ \theta = \frac{opposite}{hypotenuse}$. $sine\ 50° = \frac{AC}{6} \rightarrow 6 \times sin\ 50° = AC$

Now use a calculator to find $sine\ 50°$. $sin\ 50° \approx 0.766$

$AC = 6 \times 0.766 = 4.596$, rounding to the nearest tenth: $4.596 \approx 4.6$

22) The answer is 12 m

The width of the rectangle is twice its length. Let x be the length. Then, $width = 2x$

Perimeter of the rectangle is $2\ (width + length) = 2(2x + x) = 72 \Rightarrow 6x = 72 \Rightarrow x = 12$. The length of the rectangle's length is 12 meters.

23) The answer is $\frac{1}{25}$

Write the ratio of $5a$ to $2b$. $\frac{5a}{2b} = \frac{1}{10}$. Use cross multiplication and then simplify.

$$5a \times 10 = 2b \times 1 \rightarrow 50a = 2b \rightarrow a = \frac{2b}{50} = \frac{b}{25}$$

Now, find the ratio of a to b. $\frac{a}{b} = \frac{\frac{b}{25}}{b} \rightarrow \frac{b}{25} \div b = \frac{b}{25} \times \frac{1}{b} = \frac{b}{25b} = \frac{1}{25}$

The ratio of a to b is 1 to 25 or $\frac{1}{25}$.

24) The answer is $\frac{3}{5}$

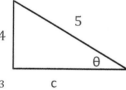

$sin\theta = \frac{opposite}{hypotenuse} = \frac{4}{5} \Rightarrow$ We have the following triangle.

Then: $c = \sqrt{5^2 - 4^2} = \sqrt{25 - 16} = \sqrt{9} = 3$, $cos\theta = \frac{adjacent}{hypotenuse} = \frac{3}{5}$

25) The answer is 225

$0.6x = (0.3) \times 20 \rightarrow x = \frac{6}{0.6} = 10 \rightarrow (x + 5)^2 = (15)^2 = 225$

26) The answer is 50 $miles$

Use the information provided in the question to draw the shape.

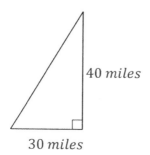

40 $miles$

30 $miles$

Use Pythagorean Theorem: $a^2 + b^2 = c^2$

$40^2 + 30^2 = c^2 \Rightarrow 1,600 + 900 = c^2 \Rightarrow 2,500 = c^2 \Rightarrow c = 50$

The boat is 50 miles far from its start point.

27) The answer is $\frac{10}{3}$

METHOD ONE

$log_4(x + 2) - log_4(x - 2) = 1$, Add $log_4(x - 2)$ to both sides

$log_4(x + 2) - log_4(x - 2) + log_4(x - 2) = 1 + log_4(x - 2)$

$log_4(x + 2) = 1 + log_4(x - 2)$

Apply logarithm rule: $a = log_b(b^a) \Rightarrow 1 = log_4(4^1) = log_4(4)$

Then: $log_4(x + 2) = log_4(4) + log_4(x - 2)$

Logarithm rule: $log_c(a) + log_c(b) = log_c(ab)$

Then: $log_4(4) + log_4(x - 2) = log_4(4(x - 2))$

$log_4(x + 2) = log_4(4(x - 2))$

When the logs have the same base: $log_b(f(x)) = log_b(g(x)) = f(x) = g(x)$

$(x + 2) = 4(x - 2)$, $x = \frac{10}{3}$

METHOD TWO

We know that: $log_a b - log_a c = log_a \frac{b}{c}$ and $log_a b = c \Rightarrow b = a^c$

Then: $log_4(x + 2) - log_4(x - 2) = log_4 \frac{x+2}{x-2} = 1 \Rightarrow \frac{x+2}{x-2} = 4^1 = 4 \Rightarrow x + 2 = 4(x - 2)$

$\Rightarrow x + 2 = 4x - 8 \Rightarrow 4x - x = 8 + 2 \rightarrow 3x = 10 \Rightarrow x = \frac{10}{3}$

28) The answer is $- x^2 - 3x - 7$

$(g - f)(x) = g(x) - f(x) = (-x^2 - 1 - 2x) - (6 + x)$

$-x^2 - 1 - 2x - 6 - x = -x^2 - 3x - 7$

29) The answer is $16\sqrt{3}cm^2$

The area of the triangle is: $\frac{1}{2} AD \times BC$ and AD is perpendicular to BC. Triangle ADC is a $30° - 60° - 90°$ right triangle. The relationship among all sides of right triangle $30° - 60° - 90°$ is provided in the following triangle: In this triangle, the opposite side of $30°$ angle is half of the hypotenuse. And the opposite side of $60°$ is opposite of $30° \times \sqrt{3}$

$CD = 4$, then: $AD = 4 \times \sqrt{3}$

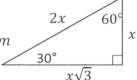

The area of the triangle ABC is: $\frac{1}{2} AD \times BC = \frac{1}{2} 4\sqrt{3} \times 8 = 16\sqrt{3}cm$

30) The answer is 105

$y = 4ab + 3b^3$. Plug in the values of a and b in the equation: $a = 2$ and $b = 3$

$y = 4(2)(3) + 3(3)^3 = 24 + 3(27) = 24 + 81 = 105$

31) The answer is $\frac{u^{10}}{96v^6w}$

First, simplify the numerator by using the exponent's rules: $(x^a)^b = x^{a \times b}$. Then:

$\frac{(4u^{-5}v^3)^{-2}}{6w} = \frac{4^{-2}u^{10}v^{-6}}{96w}$. Now, use negative exponent's rule: $\left(\frac{x^a}{x^b}\right)^{-2} = \left(\frac{x^b}{x^a}\right)^2$

Then: $\frac{4^{-2}u^{10}v^{-6}}{96w} = \frac{u^{10}}{(4^2)(6w)(v^6)} = \frac{u^{10}}{96v^6w}$

32) The answer is $x = \frac{16}{5}$ or $x = 3.2$

First, find a common denominator for 3 and $\frac{2x}{x-7}$. It's $x - 7$. Then:

$$3 + \frac{2x}{x-7} = \frac{3(x-7)}{x-7} + \frac{2x}{x-7} = \frac{3x - 21 + 2x}{x-7} = \frac{5x - 21}{x-7}$$

Now, multiply the numerator and denominator of $\frac{5}{7-x}$ by -1. Then:

$\frac{5 \times (-1)}{(7-x) \times (-1)} = \frac{-5}{x-7}$. Rewrite the expression: $\frac{5x-21}{x-7} = \frac{-5}{x-7}$. Since the denominators of both fractions are equal, then, the numerators must be equal.

$$5x - 21 = -5 \rightarrow 5x = 16 \rightarrow x = \frac{16}{5}$$

33) The answer is $-2 < x < 6$

Since this inequality contains absolute value, then, the value inside absolute value bars is greater than -32 and less than 32. Then:

$|16 - 8x| < 32 \rightarrow -32 < 16 - 8x < 32 \rightarrow -32 - 16 < 16 - 8x - 16 < 32 - 16 \rightarrow$
$-48 < -8x < 16$. Now, divide all sides by -8. (remember: For dividing or multiplying both sides by negative numbers, flip the direction of the inequality sign.)

$\frac{-48}{-8} > \frac{-8x}{-8} > \frac{16}{-8} \rightarrow 6 > x > -2$ or $-2 > x < 6$

34) The answer is $-\frac{8}{145} - \frac{96}{145}i$

To rationalize this imaginary expression, multiply both numerator and denominator by the conjugate $\frac{12-i}{12-i}$. Then: $\frac{-8i}{12+i} = \frac{-8i(12-i)}{(12+i)(12-i)} =$

Apply complex arithmetic rule: $(a + bi)(a - bi) = a^2 + b^2$. Then:

$$\frac{-8i(12 - i)}{(12 + i)(12 - i)} = \frac{-96i + 8i^2}{12^2 + 1^2} = \frac{-96i - 8}{145} = -\frac{8}{145} - \frac{96}{145}i$$

35) The answer is on the following graph

First, simplify the inequality: $2y > 4x^2 \rightarrow \frac{2y}{2} > \frac{4x^2}{2} \rightarrow y > 2x^2$

Now, graph the quadratic $y = 2x^2$

Plug in some values for x and solve for y.

$x = 0 \rightarrow y = 2(0)^2 = 0$, $x = 1 \rightarrow y = 2(1)^2 = 2$, $x = -1 \rightarrow y = 2(-1)^2 = 2$

$x = 2 \rightarrow y = 2(2)^2 = 4$, $x = -2 \rightarrow y = 2(-2)^2 = 4$

Since the inequality sing is greater than ($>$), we need to use dash lines.

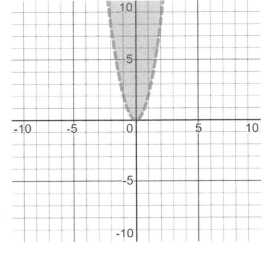

Now, choose a testing point inside the parabola. Let's choose $(0, 2)$.

$$y > 2x^2 \rightarrow 2 > 2(0)^2 \rightarrow 2 > 0$$

This is true. So, inside the parabola is the solution section.

ALEKS Mathematics Practice Test 2

1) **The answer is** $(2x - 7)(2x + 7)$

Rewrite 4 as 2^2: $4x^2 = 2^2 x^2$. Rewrite 49 as 7^2. Now, apply exponent rule: $a^m b^m = (ab)^m$. Then: $2^2 x^2 = (2x)^2$. Apply difference of two square formula: $x^2 - y^2 = (x - y)(x + y) \rightarrow 4x^2 - 49 = (2x)^2 - 7^2 = (2x - 7)(2x + 7)$

2) **The answer is** $x = 0$ **or** $x = 4$

To solve for x, divide both sides by 7. Then: $7x^2 - 28x = 0 \rightarrow \frac{7x^2}{7} - \frac{28x}{7} = \frac{0}{7} \rightarrow$ $x^2 - 4x = 0$. Now, take the common factor x out: $x^2 - 4x = 0 \rightarrow x(x - 4) = 0$

The product of x and $(x - 4)$ is zero. Therefore, x is zero or $(x - 4)$ is zero. Then: $x = 0$ or $x - 4 = 0 \rightarrow x = 4$

3) **The answers are 13** *and* **15**

Let's put x for smaller integer. Then, the two integers are x and $x + 2$. (the difference of any two consecutive odd (or even) integers is 2). The sum of two integers is 28. Write the equation and solve for x:

$$x + (x + 2) = 28 \rightarrow 2x + 2 = 28 \rightarrow 2x = 26 \rightarrow \frac{2x}{2} = \frac{26}{2} \rightarrow x = 13$$

The smaller integer is 13 and the bigger integer is 15 ($13 + 2 = 15$).

4) **The answers are: Slope is** -4 **and** y**-intercept is** -2

Write the equation in slope intercept form. The slope intercept form of the equation of a line is: $y = mx + b$. Then: $-8x - 2y = 4 \rightarrow -8x - 2y + 8x = 4 + 8x \rightarrow$

$$-2y = 8x + 4 \rightarrow \frac{-2y}{-2} = \frac{8x}{-2} + \frac{4}{-2} \rightarrow y = -4x - 2 \rightarrow$$

The slope intercept form of the line is: $y = -4x - 2$.

Then, the slope is -4 and the y $-$intercept is -2.

Now, you can graph the line.

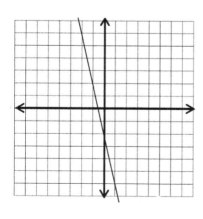

5) The answer is: Domain: all real values of x, range: all real number where $f(x) \geq 2$

The domain of $f(x)$ is "all real values of x. (x can be any real number)

Range: since x^2 is never negative, $x^2 + 2$ is never less than 2.

Hence, the range of $f(x)$ is "all real numbers where $f(x) \geq 2$".

6) The answer is 3

Solving systems of equations by elimination: Multiply the first equation by (-2), then add it to the second equation.

$$\begin{array}{c} -2(2x + 5y = 11) \\ \underline{4x - 2y = -14} \end{array} \Rightarrow \begin{array}{c} -4x - 10y = -22 \\ 4x - 2y = -14 \end{array} \Rightarrow -12y = -36 \Rightarrow y = 3$$

7) The answer is $x = 7$

$log_3(x + 20) - log_3(x + 2) = 1$. First, condense the two logarithms:

$$log_3(x + 20) - log_3(x + 2) = 1 \rightarrow log_3\left(\frac{x + 20}{x + 2}\right) = 1$$

We know that $log_a a = 1$. Then: $log_3\left(\frac{x+20}{x+2}\right) = log_3 3 \rightarrow \frac{x+20}{x+2} = 3$

Now, use cross multiplication and solve for x.

$$\frac{x + 20}{x + 2} = 3 \rightarrow x + 20 = 3(x + 2) \rightarrow x + 20 = 3x + 6 \rightarrow 14 = 2x \rightarrow x = 7$$

8) The answer is $\frac{-12y-55a}{12a}$

To write this expression as a single fraction, we need to find a common denominator.

The common denominator of $12a$ and $8a$ is $24a$. Then:

$$-4 + \frac{2a - 6y}{12a} - \frac{6a + 4y}{8a} = \frac{-4(24a)}{24a} + \frac{2(2a - 6y)}{24a} - \frac{3(6a + 4y)}{24a}$$

Now, simplify the numerators and combine:

$$\frac{-4(24a)}{24a} + \frac{2(2a - 6y)}{24a} - \frac{3(6a + 4y)}{24a} = \frac{-96a}{24a} + \frac{4a - 12y}{24a} - \frac{18a + 12y}{24a} =$$

$$\frac{-96a + 4a - 12y - 18a - 12y}{24a} = \frac{-110a - 24y}{24a}$$

Divide both numerator and denominator by 2. Then:

$$\frac{-110a - 24y}{24a} = \frac{-12y - 55a}{12a}$$

9) The answer is -15

$g(x) = -3$, then $f\big(g(x)\big) = f(-3) = 2\,(-3)^3 + 5(-3)^2 + 2(-3) = -54 + 45 - 6 = -15$

10) The answer is $\frac{8\sqrt{\pi}}{\pi}$

Formula for the area of a circle is: $A = \pi r^2$, using 64 for the area of the circle we have:

$64 = \pi r^2$. Solve for the radius (r). $\frac{64}{\pi} = r^2 \rightarrow r = \sqrt{\frac{64}{\pi}} = \frac{8}{\sqrt{\pi}} = \frac{8}{\sqrt{\pi}} \times \frac{\sqrt{\pi}}{\sqrt{\pi}} = \frac{8\sqrt{\pi}}{\pi}$

11) The answer is $\frac{1}{2}$

The relationship among all sides of right triangle $30° - 60° - 90°$ is provided in the

following triangle: Sine of $30°$ equals to: $\frac{opposite}{hypotenuse} = \frac{x}{2x} = \frac{1}{2}$

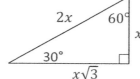

12) The answer is $145°$

The angle x and 35 are supplementary angles. Therefore: $x + 35 = 180 \rightarrow$

$$x = 180° - 35° = 145°$$

13) The answer is $30°$

The sum of supplement angles is 180. Let x be that angle. Therefore, $x + 5x = 180$

$6x = 180$, divide both sides by 6: $x = 30$ degrees

14) The answer is $\frac{3}{4} + i$

To simplify the fraction, multiply both numerator and denominator by i.

$\frac{4-3i}{-4i} \times \frac{i}{i} = \frac{4i-3i^2}{-4i^2}$, $i^2 = -1$, Then: $\frac{4i-3i^2}{-4i^2} = \frac{4i-3(-1)}{-4(-1)} = \frac{4i+3}{4} = \frac{4i}{4} + \frac{3}{4} = \frac{3}{4} + i$

15) The answer is 38

Let x be the smallest number. Then, these are the numbers: $x, x + 1, x + 2, x + 3,$

and $x + 4$. $average = \frac{sum\ of\ terms}{number\ of\ terms} \Rightarrow 40 = \frac{x+(x+1)+(x+2)+(x+3)+(x+4)}{5} \Rightarrow 40 = \frac{5x+10}{5} \Rightarrow$

$200 = 5x + 10 \Rightarrow 190 = 5x \Rightarrow x = 38$

The smallest number is 38.

16) The answer is $\frac{\sqrt{15}}{4}$

$sinA = \frac{1}{4} \Rightarrow$ Since $sin\theta = \frac{opposite}{hypotenuse}$, we have the following right triangle. Then:

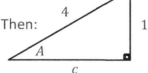

$c = \sqrt{4^2 - 1^2} = \sqrt{16 - 1} = \sqrt{15}$

$$cosA = \frac{adjacent}{hypotenuse} = \frac{\sqrt{15}}{4}$$

17) The answer is 16π

The equation of a circle in standard form is: $(x - h)^2 + (y - k)^2 = r^2$, where r is the radius of the circle. In this circle the radius is 4. $r^2 = 16 \rightarrow r = 4$, $(x + 2)^2 + (y - 4)^2 = 16$, Area of a circle: $A = \pi r^2 = \pi(4)^2 = 16\pi$

18) The answer is $-\frac{1}{2}$

The equation of a line in slope intercept form is: $y = mx + b$, Solve for y. $4x - 2y = 14 \Rightarrow -2y = 14 - 4x \Rightarrow y = \frac{(14-4x)}{-2} \Rightarrow y = 2x - 7$, The slope of the line is 2. The slope of the line perpendicular to this line is: $m_1 \times m_2 = -1 \Rightarrow 2 \times m_2 = -1 \Rightarrow m_2 = -\frac{1}{2}$

19) The answer is $\frac{2}{x^3} + 4$

$g(x) = \frac{1}{x}$. To find $f(g(x))$, substitute x with $\frac{1}{x}$ in the function $f(x)$. Then:

$f(g(x)) = f\left(\frac{1}{x}\right) = 2 \times (\frac{1}{x})^3 + 4 = \frac{2}{x^3} + 4$

20) The answer is 45

First, find the number. Let x be the number. Write the equation and solve for x. 150% of a number is 75, then: $1.5 \times x = 75 \Rightarrow x = 75 \div 1.5 = 50$, 90% of 50 is: $0.9 \times 50 = 45$

21) The answer is 1

The cotangent is the reciprocal of tangent: $tangent\ \beta = \dfrac{1}{cotangent\ \beta} = \dfrac{1}{1} = 1$

22) The answer is $\dfrac{3}{4}x$

Find the common denominator and simplify the expression.

$$\sqrt{\frac{x^2}{2} + \frac{x^2}{16}} = \sqrt{\frac{8x^2}{16} + \frac{x^2}{16}} = \sqrt{\frac{9x^2}{16}} = \sqrt{\frac{9}{16}x^2} = \sqrt{\frac{9}{16}} \times \sqrt{x^2} = \frac{3}{4} \times x = \frac{3}{4}x$$

23) The answer is $\dfrac{8}{17}$

$tan\theta = \dfrac{opposite}{adjacent}$, and $\tan x = \dfrac{8}{15}$, therefore, the opposite side of the angle x is 8 and the

adjacent side is 15. Let's draw the triangle.

Using Pythagorean theorem, we have: $a^2 + b^2 = c^2 \rightarrow 8^2 + 15^2 = c^2 \rightarrow 64 + 225 =$

$c^2 \rightarrow c = 17$, $\sin x = \dfrac{opposite}{hypotenuse} = \dfrac{8}{17}$

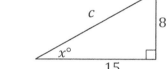

24) The answer is 1

The function $f(x)$ is undefined when the denominator of $\dfrac{1}{(x-3)^2+4(x-3)+4}$ is equal to zero.

The expression $(x-3)^2 + 4(x-3) + 4$ is a perfect square.

$(x-3)^2 + 4(x-3) + 4 = ((x-3)+2)^2$ which can be rewritten as $(x-1)^2$. The

expression $(x-1)^2$ is equal to zero if and only if $x = 1$. Therefore, the value of x for

which $f(x)$ is undefined is 1.

25) The answers are $0, -2, -4$

Frist factor the function: $f(x) = x^3 + 6x^2 + 8x = x\ (x+4)(x+2)$, To find the zeros, $f(x)$

should be zero. $f(x) = x\ (x+4)(x+2) = 0$, Therefore, the zeros are: $x = 0$,

$(x+4) = 0 \Rightarrow x = -4, (x+2) = 0 \Rightarrow x = -2$

26) The answer is $\dfrac{12x-3}{x^3}$

First find a common denominator for both fractions in the expression $\dfrac{5}{x^2} + \dfrac{7x-3}{x^3}$.

The common denominator is x^3. Now, we can combine like terms into a single numerator over the denominator:

$$\frac{5x}{x^3} + \frac{7x - 3}{x^3} = \frac{5x + (7x - 3)}{x^3} = \frac{12x - 3}{x^3}$$

27) The answer is 25

The angles on a straight line add up to 180 degrees. Then: $x + 25 + y + 2x + y = 180$

$\rightarrow 3x + 2y = 180 - 25, x = 35 \rightarrow 3(35) + 2y = 155 \rightarrow 2y = 155 - 105 = 50 \rightarrow y = 25$

28) The answer is $n^2 + 4n + 11$

$(3n^2 + 4n + 6) - (2n^2 - 5)$. Combine like terms together: $3n^2 - 2n^2 = n^2$

$$6 - (-5) = 11$$

Combine these terms into one expression to find the answer:

$$(3n^2 + 4n + 6) - (2n^2 - 5) = n^2 + 4n + 11$$

29) The answer is $28\ in$

Let x be the width of the rectangle. Use Pythagorean Theorem: $a^2 + b^2 = c^2$

$x^2 + 8^2 = 10^2 \Rightarrow x^2 + 64 = 100 \Rightarrow x^2 = 100 - 64 = 36 \Rightarrow x = 6$

The width of the rectangle is 6 inches. Then:

The perimeter of the rectangle $= 2\ (length + width) = 2\ (8 + 6) = 2\ (14) = 28\ in$

30) The answer is 1.02

The initial deposit earns 2 percent interest compounded annually. Thus, at the end of year 1, the new value of the account is the initial deposit of $150 plus 2 percent of the initial deposit: $150 + \frac{2}{100}(\$150) = \$150(1.02)$.

Since the interest is compounded annually, the value at the end of each succeeding year is the sum of the previous year's value plus 2 percent of the previous year's value. This is equivalent to multiplying the previous year's value by 1.02. Thus, after 2 years, the value will be $150(1.02)(1.02) = \$(150)(1.02)^2$; and after 3 years, the value will be $(150)(1.02)^3$; and after n years, the value will be $(150)(1.02)^n$. Therefore, in the formula for the value for Sara's account after n years $(100)(x)^n$, the value of x is 1.02.

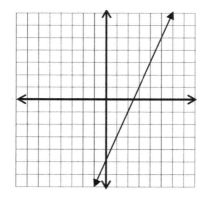

31) The answer is on the graph

To graph this line, we need to find two points. When x is zero the value of y is -5. And when y is 0 the value of x is 2.5.

$$x = 0 \rightarrow y + 3 = 2(0 - 1) \rightarrow y = -5$$

$$y = 0 \rightarrow 0 + 3 = 2(x - 1) \rightarrow x = 2.5$$

Now, we have two points:

$(0, -5)$ and $(2.5, 0)$.

Find the points on the coordinate plane and graph the line. Remember that the slope of the line is 2.

32) The answer is $215 + 45i$

Use the FOIL (First, Out, In, Last) method to multiply two imaginary expressions:

$$(-7)(-5) + (-7)(-15i) + (12i)(-5) + (12i)(-15i) = 35 + 105i - 60i - 180i^2$$

Combine like terms $(+105i - 60i)$ and simplify:

$$35 + 105i - 60i - 180i^2 = 35 - 45i - 180i^2$$

$i^2 = -1$, then: $35 - 45i - 180i^2 = 35 - 45i - 180(-1) = 35 - 45i + 180 = 215 + 45i$

33) The answer is $log\, s + \frac{1}{2} log\, t - 2\, log\, r$

Use logarithms rule: $log_a\, x - log_a\, y = log_a \frac{x}{y}$. Then: $log \frac{s\sqrt{t}}{r^2} = log\, s\sqrt{t} - log\, r^2$

Using the logarithms rule: $log_a(x \cdot y) = log_a\, x + log_a\, y$, we get: $log\, s\sqrt{t} = log\, s + log\, \sqrt{t}$

We know that $\sqrt{t} = t^{\frac{1}{2}}$. Then: $log\, s + log\, \sqrt{t} = log\, s + log\, \sqrt{t} = log\, s + log\, t^{\frac{1}{2}}$

Now, use logarithms rule: $log_a\, x^n = n\, log_a\, x$. Then: $log\, t^{\frac{1}{2}} = \frac{1}{2} log\, t$ and $log\, r^2 = 2\, log\, r$

Finally: $log(s\sqrt{t}) - log(r^2) = log\, s + \frac{1}{2} log\, t - 2\, log\, r$

34) The answer is $2(x - 6)(x + 6)$ or $2x^2 - 72$

Find the factors of the denominators: $\frac{3x}{x^2-36} = \frac{3x}{(x-6)(x+6)}$ and $\frac{4}{2x-12} = \frac{4}{2(x-6)}$

Since the factor $(x - 6)$ is common in both denominators, then, the least common denominator is: $2(x - 6)(x + 6) = 2x^2 - 72$

35) The answer is 3.9

To find AC, use sine B. Then:

$sine\, \theta = \frac{opposite}{hypotenuse}$. $sine\, 40° = \frac{AC}{6} \rightarrow 6 \times sine\, 40° = AC$,

Now use a calculator to find $sine\, 40°$. $sine\, 40° \approx 0.643 \rightarrow AC \approx 3.86$

Receive the PDF version of this book or get another FREE book!

Thank you for using our Book!

Do you LOVE this book?

Then, you can get the PDF version of this book or another book absolutely FREE!

Please email us at:

info@EffortlessMath.com

for details.

Author's Final Note

I hope you enjoyed reading this book. You've made it through the book! Great job!

First of all, thank you for purchasing this practice book. I know you could have picked any number of books to help you prepare for your ALEKS Math test, but you picked this book and for that I am extremely grateful.

It took me years to write this workbook for the ALKES Math because I wanted to prepare a comprehensive ALKES Math workbook to help test takers make the most effective use of their valuable time while preparing for the test.

After teaching and tutoring math courses for over a decade, I've gathered my personal notes and lessons to develop this practice book. It is my greatest hope that the exercises in this book could help you prepare for your test successfully.

If you have any questions, please contact me at reza@effortlessmath.com and I will be glad to assist. Your feedback will help me to greatly improve the quality of my books in the future and make this book even better. Furthermore, I expect that I have made a few minor errors somewhere in this book. If you think this to be the case, please let me know so I can fix the issue as soon as possible.

If you enjoyed this book and found some benefit in reading this, I'd like to hear from you and hope that you could take a quick minute to post a review on the book's Amazon page. To leave your valuable feedback, please visit: amzn.to/34fu0TM

Or scan this QR code.

I personally go over every single review, to make sure my books really are reaching out and helping students and test takers. Please help me help ALEKS Math test takers, by leaving a review!

I wish you all the best in your future success!

Reza Nazari

Math teacher and author

Made in the USA
Columbia, SC
20 January 2023

10788913R00135